Keto Veg Bible

The Essential Vegetarian Keto Cookbook:

Keto Diet for Vegetarians

Ketogenic and Intermittent Fasting Diet

Keto Diet for Vegetarians Athletes

Sebi Alan Guntry

Tables of contains

Keto Diet for Vegetarians

The Best Keto Diet for Vegetarians to Burn Fat and Lose 20 Pounds in 15 Days with Delicious Recipes.

<u>Sebi Alan Guntry</u>

Introduction

A Keto diet for vegetarians, is focused on proportionately eating more foods primarily from plants and cutting back on animal-derived foods. However, it does not necessarily involve eliminating entire food groups and lean sources of protein. This means, those on a plant-based diet may still opt to eat some meat.

Going vegan, on the other hand, means being strictly against animal products in any form—from never eating meat and dairy products to not patronizing products tested on animals and not wearing animal products such as leather.

A healthy plant-based diet generally emphasizes meeting your nutritional needs by eating more whole plant foods, while reducing the intake of animal products. Whole foods refer to natural, unrefined or minimally refined foods. Plant foods consist of those that do not have animal ingredients such as meat, eggs, honey, milk and other dairy products.

In contrast, those on a vegetarian diet may still eat processed and refined foods. Vegetarians can even eat fast foods, junk food and other salty snacks guilt-free.

Once you get started with this diet, you will notice a huge difference in how you feel each day. From the time that you wake up in the morning, you will feel that you have more energy, and that you do not get tired as easily as before. You will also have more mental focus and fewer mood-related problems.

As for digestion, a plant-based diet is also said to improve how the digestive system works. In fact, dieters confirm fewer incidences of stomach pains, bloating, indigestion and hyperacidity.

Then there's the weight loss benefit that we cannot forget about. Since a plant-based diet means eating fruits, vegetables, and whole grains that have fewer calories and are lower in fat, you will enjoy weight loss benefits that some other fad diets are not able to provide.

Aside from helping you lose weight; it maintains ideal weight longer because this diet is easier to sustain and does not require elimination of certain food groups.

Don't worry about not getting enough nutrients from your food intake. This diet provides all the necessary nutrients including proteins, vitamins, minerals, carbohydrates, fats, and antioxidants. And again, that's because it does not eliminate any food group but only encourages you to focus more on plant-based food products.

As you can imagine, humans have been consuming a plant-based diet before the invention of McDonald's and some of our other favorite fast-food chains. To begin our journey, I am going to start us off in the times of the hunter-gatherer. While we could go back even further (think Ancient Egypt!), I believe this is where a plant-based diet becomes most relevant.

The hunter-gatherer time period is where we find the earliest evidence of hunting. While we do have a long history of eating meat, this was a point in time where consuming meat was very limited. Of course, humans eating meat does not mean we were carnivores; in fact, the way we are built tells us differently. Yes, we can consume meat, but humans are considered omnivores. You can tell this from our jaw design, running speeds, alimentary tract, and the fact we don't have claws attached to our fingers. History also tells us we are omnivores by nature; however, the evolution of our human brains led us to become hunters so that we could survive.

The need for hunting did not come around until our ancestors left tropical regions. Other locations influenced the availability of plant-based foods. Instead of enduring winter with limited amounts of food, we had to adapt! Of course, out of hunger, animal-flesh becomes much more appealing. This early in time, our ancestors did not have a grocery store to just pop in and buy whatever they needed. Instead, they used the opportunity of hunting and gathering to keep themselves alive.

Eventually, we moved away from hunting and gathering and started to become farmers. While this timeline is a bit tricky and agricultural history began at different points in different parts of the world, all that matters is that at some point; animals started to become domesticated and dairy, eggs, and meat all became readily available. Once this started, humans no longer needed to hunt nor gather because the farmers provided everything we could desire

While starting a plant-based diet is an excellent idea and has many wonderful benefits let's be honest, you are mostly here to benefit yourself. It is fantastic that you are deciding to put you and your health first. You deserve to be the best version of yourself, with a little bit of legwork, you will be there in no time

To some people, a plant-based diet is just another fad diet. There are so many diets on the market right now, why is plant-based any different? Whether you are looking to lose weight, reverse disease, or just love animals.

A plant-based diet is so much more than just eating fruits and vegetables. This is a lifestyle where you are encouraged to journey to a better version of yourself. As you improve your eating habits, you will need something to do with all of your new found energy! It is time to gain control over your eating habits and figure out how food truly does affect our daily lives! Below, you will find the amazing benefits a plant-based diet has to offer you.

Breakfast

Pumpkin pancakes

Preparation Time: 15 minutes

Cooking Time: 15 minutes

Servings: 4

Ingredients

- 2 cups unsweetened almond milk
- 1 teaspoon apple cider vinegar
- 2½ cups whole-wheat flour
- 2 tablespoons baking powder
- ½ Teaspoon baking soda
- 1 teaspoon sea salt
- 1 teaspoon pumpkin pie spice or ½ teaspoon ground -cinnamon plus ¼ teaspoon grated -nutmeg plus ¼ teaspoon ground allspice
- ½ Cup canned pumpkin purée
- 1 cup water
- 1 tablespoon coconut oil

Directions

In a small bowl, combine the almond milk and apple cider vinegar. Set aside.

In a bowl, whisk together the flour, baking powder, baking soda, salt, and pumpkin pie spice. In bowl, combine the almond milk mixture, pumpkin purée, and water, whisking to mix well. Mix the wet Ingredients to the dry Ingredients and fold together until the dry -Ingredients are just moistened.

In a nonstick pan or griddle over medium-high heat, melt the coconut oil and swirl to coat. Pour the batter into the pan ¼ cup at a time and cook until the pancakes are browned, about 5 minutes per side. Serve immediately.

Nutrition

- calories 270
- fat 15,
- fiber 3
- carbs 5
- protein 9

Quinoa Applesauce Muffins

Preparation Time: 10 minutes

Cooking Time: 15 minutes

Servings: 5

Ingredients

2 tablespoons coconut oil or margarine, melted, plus more for coating the muffin tin

¼ Cup ground flaxseed

½ Cup water

2 cups unsweetened applesauce

½ Cup brown sugar

1 teaspoon apple cider vinegar

2½ cups whole-grain flour

1½ cups cooked quinoa

2 teaspoons baking soda

Pinch salt

½ Cup dried cranberries or raisins

Directions

Preheat the oven to 400°f.

Coat a muffin tin with coconut oil, line with paper muffin cups, or use a nonstick tin. In a large bowl, stir together the flaxseed and water. Add the applesauce, sugar, coconut oil, and vinegar. Stir to combine. Add the flour, quinoa, baking soda, and salt, stirring until just combined. Gently fold in the cranberries without stirring too much. Scoop the muffin mixture into the prepared tin, about ⅓ cup for each muffin.

Bake for 15 to 20 minutes, until slightly browned on top and springy to the touch. Let cool for about 10 minutes. Run a dinner knife around the inside of each cup to loosen, then tilt the muffins on their sides in the muffin wells so air gets underneath. These keep in an airtight container in the refrigerator for up to 1 week or in the freezer indefinitely.

Nutrition

calories: 387

protein: 7g

total fat: 5g

saturated fat: 2g

carbohydrates: 57g

fiber: 8g

Green breakfast smoothie

Preparation Time: 10 minutes

Cooking Time: 0 minutes

Servings: 2

Ingredients

- ½ Banana, sliced
- 2 cups spinach or other greens, such as kale
- 1 cup sliced berries of your choosing, fresh or frozen
- 1 orange, peeled and cut into segments
- 1 cup unsweetened nondairy milk
- 1 cup ice

Directions

In a blender, combine all the Ingredients. Starting with the blender on low speed, begin blending the smoothie, gradually increasing blender speed until smooth. Serve immediately.

Nutrition

calories 270

fat 15

fiber 3

carbs 5

protein 9

Blueberry Lemonade Smoothie

Preparation Time : 10 minutes

Cooking Time: 10 minutes

Servings: 1

Ingredients

- 1 cup roughly chopped kale
- ¾ Cup frozen blueberries
- 1 cup unsweetened soy or almond milk
- Juice of 1 lemon

- 1 tablespoon maple syrup

Directions

Combine all the Ingredients in a blender and blend until smooth. Enjoy immediately.

Nutrition

- Calories; 398
- Fat 21g
- Carbs 4.7g
- Proteins 44.2g
- Sugars 0.5g

Berry Protein Smoothie

Preparation Time: 5 minutes

Cooking Time: 0 minutes

Servings: 1

Ingredients

- 1 banana
- 1 cup fresh or frozen berries
- ¾ Cup water or nondairy milk, plus more as needed
- 1 scoop plant-based protein powder, 3 ounces silken tofu, ¼ cup rolled oats, or ½ cup cooked quinoa
- Additions
- 1 tablespoon ground flaxseed or chia seeds
- 1 handful fresh spinach or lettuce, or 1 chunk cucumber
- Coconut water to replace some of the liquid

Directions

In a blender, combine the banana, berries, water,

and your choice of protein.

Add any addition Ingredients as desired. Purée until smooth and creamy, about 50 seconds.

Add a bit more water if you like a thinner smoothie.

Nutrition

- calories: 332
- protein: 7g
- total fat: 5g
- saturated fat: 1g
- carbohydrates: 72g
- fiber: 11g

Almond Plum Oats Overnight

Preparation Time: 10 minutes

Cooking Time: 10 minutes plus overnight

Servings: 2

Ingredients

- Rolled oats: 60g
- Plums: 3 ripe and chopped
- Almond milk: 300ml
- Chia seeds: 1 tbsp
- Nutmeg: a pinch
- Vanilla extract: a few drops
- Whole almonds: 1 tbsp roughly chopped

Directions:

1. Add oats, nutmeg, vanilla extract, almond milk, and chia seeds to a bowl and mix well
2. Add in cubed plums and cover and place in the fridge for a night
3. Mix the oats well morning and add into the serving bowl
4. Serve with your favorite toppings

Nutrition

- Carbs: 24.7g

- Protein: 9.5g
- Fats: 10.8g
- Calories: 248Kcal

Avocado Miso Chickpeas Toast

Preparation Time: 10 minutes

Cooking Time: 15 minutes

Servings: 2

Ingredients

- Chickpeas: 400g drained and rinsed
- Avocado: 1 medium
- Toasted sesame oil: 1 tsp
- White miso paste: 1 ½ tbsp
- Sesame seeds: 1 tbsp
- Spring onion: 1 finely sliced
- Lemon:1 half for the juice and half wedged to serve
- Rye bread: 4 slices toasted

Directions:

1. In a bowl add sesame oil, chickpeas, miso, and lemon juice and mash using a potato masher

2. Roughly crushed avocado in another bowl using a fork
3. Add the avocado to the chickpeas and make a spread
4. Spread it on a toast and top with spring onion and sesame seeds
5. Serve with lemon wedges

Nutrition

- Carbs: 33.3 g
- Protein:14.6 g
- Fats: 26.6 g
- Calories: 456 Kcal

Banana Malt Bread

Preparation Time: 10 minutes

Cooking Time: 1 hour 20 minutes and Maturing Time

Servings: 12 slices

Ingredients

- Hot strong black tea: 120ml
- Malt extract: 150g plus extra for brushing
- Bananas:2 ripe mashed
- Sultanas: 100g
- Pitted dates:120g chopped

- Plain flour: 250g
- Soft dark brown sugar: 50g
- Baking powder: 2 tsp

Directions:

1. Preheat the oven to 140C
2. Line the loaf tin with the baking paper
3. Brew tea and include sultanas and dates to it
4. Take a small pan and heat the malt extract and gradually add sugar to it
5. Stir continuously and let it cook
6. In a bowl, add flour, salt, and baking powder and now top with sugar extract, fruits, bananas, and tea
7. Mix the batter well and add to the loaf tin
8. Bake the mixture for an hour
9. Brush the bread with extra malt extract and let it cool down before removing from the tin
10. When done, wrap in a foil; it can be consumed for a week

Nutrition

- Carbs: 43.3 g
- Protein: 3.4 g
- Fats: 0.3 g
- Calories: 194 Kcal

Banana Vegan Bread

Preparation Time: 15 minutes

Cooking Time: 1 hour 15 minutes

Servings: 1 loaf

Ingredients

- Overripe banana: 3 large mashed
- All-purpose flour: 200 g

- Unsweetened non-dairy milk: 50 ml
- White vinegar: ½ tsp
- Ground flaxseed: 10 g
- Ground cinnamon: ¼ tsp
- Granulated sugar: 140 g
- Vanilla: ¼ tsp
- Baking powder: ¼ tsp
- Baking soda: ¼ tsp
- Salt: ¼ tsp
- Canola oil: 3 tbsp
- Chopped walnuts: ½ cup

Directions:

1. Preheat the oven to 350F and line the loaf pan with parchment paper
2. Mash bananas using a fork
3. Take a large bowl, and add in mash bananas, canola oil, oat milk, sugar, vinegar, vanilla, and ground flax seed
4. Also whisk in baking powder, cinnamon, flour, and salt
5. Add batter to the loaf pan and bake for 50 minutes

6. Remove from pan and let it sit for 10 minutes

7. Slice when completely cooled down

Nutrition

- Carbs: 40.3g
- Protein: 2.8g
- Fats: 8.2g
- Calories: 240Kcal

Berry Compote

Pancakes

Preparation Time: 5 minutes

Cooking Time: 30 minutes

Servings: 2

Ingredients

- Mixed frozen berries: 200g
- Plain flour: 140 g
- Unsweetened almond milk: 140ml
- Icing sugar: 1 tbsp
- Lemon juice: 1 tbsp
- Baking powder: 2 tsp
- Vanilla extract: a dash
- Salt: a pinch
- Caster sugar: 2 tbsp
- Vegetable oil: ½ tbsp

Directions:

1. Take a small pan and add berries, lemon juice, and icing sugar
2. Cook the mixture for 10 minutes to give it a saucy texture and set aside
3. Take a bowl and add caster sugar, flour, baking powder, and salt and mix well

4. Add in almond milk and vanilla and combine well to make a batter

5. Take a non-stick pan, and heat 2 teaspoons oil in it and spread it over the whole surface

6. Add ¼ cup of the batter to the pan and cook each side for 3-4 minutes

7. Serve with compote

Nutrition

- Carbs: 92 g
- Protein: 9.4 g
- Fats: 5.2 g
- Calories: 463 Kcal

Buckwheat Crepes

Preparation Time: 15 minutes

Cooking Time: 25 minutes

Servings: 12

Ingredients

- Raw buckwheat flour: 1 cup
- Light coconut milk: 1 and 3/4 cups
- Ground cinnamon: 1/8 tsp
- Flaxseeds: 3/4 tbsp
- Melted coconut oil: 1 tbsp
- Sea salt: a pinch
- Any sweetener: as per your taste

Directions:

1. Take a bowl and add flaxseed, coconut milk, salt, avocado, and cinnamon
2. Mix them all well and fold in the flour
3. Now take a nonstick pan and pour oil and provide gentle heat
4. Add a big spoon of a mixture
5. Cook till it appears bubbly, then change side

6. Perform the task until all crepes are prepared

7. For enhancing the taste, add the sweetener of your liking

Nutrition

Carbs: 8g

Protein: 1g

Fats: 3g

Calories: 71Kcal

Chickpeas Spread Sourdough Toast

Preparation Time: 15 minutes

Cooking Time: 15 minutes

Servings: 4

Ingredients

- Chickpeas: 1 cup rinsed and drained
- Pumpkin puree: 1 cup
- Vegan yogurt: ½ cup
- Salt: as per your need
- Sourdough: 4 slices toasted

Directions:

1. In a bowl add chickpeas and pumpkin puree and mash using a potato masher
2. Add in salt and yogurt and mix
3. Spread it on a toast and serve

Nutrition

- Carbs: 33.7g
- Protein: 8.45g
- Fats: 2.5g
- Calories: 187Kcal

Chickpeas with Harissa

Preparation Time: 15 minutes

Cooking Time: 20 minutes

Servings: 2

Ingredients

- Chickpeas: 1 cup can rinse and drained well
- Onion: 1 small diced
- Cucumber: 1 cup diced
- Tomato: 1 cup diced
- Salt: as per your taste
- Lemon juice: 2 tbsp
- Harissa: 2 tsp
- Olive oil: 1 tbsp
- Flat-leaf parsley: 2 tbsp chopped

Directions:

1. Add lemon juice, harissa, and olive oil in a bowl and whisk

2. Take a serving bowl and add onion, cucumber, chickpeas, salt and the sauce you made

3. Add parsley from the top and serve

Nutrition

- Carbs: 55.6 g
- Protein: 17.8g
- Fats: 11.8g
- Calories: 398Kcal

Lunch

Whipped Potatoes

Preparation Time: 20 minutes

Cooking Time: 35 minutes

Servings: 10

Ingredients

- 4 cups water
- 3 lb. potatoes, sliced into cubes
- 3 cloves garlic, crushed
- 6 tablespoons butter
- 2 bay leaves
- 10 sage leaves
- ½ cup Greek yogurt
- ¼ cup low-fat milk
- Salt to taste

Direction

1. Boil the potatoes in water for 30 minutes or until tender.
2. Drain.
3. In a pan over medium heat, cook the garlic in butter for 1 minute.
4. Add the sage and cook for 5 more minutes.
5. Discard the garlic.
6. Use a fork to mash the potatoes.
7. Whip using an electric mixer while gradually adding the butter, yogurt, and milk.
8. Season with salt.

Nutrition

- Calories: 169
- Total fat: 7.6g
- Saturated fat: 4.7g
- Cholesterol: 21mg
- Sodium: 251mg

Quinoa Avocado Salad

Preparation Time: 15 minutes

Cooking Time: 4 minutes

Servings: 4

Ingredients

- 2 tablespoons balsamic vinegar
- ¼ cup cream
- ¼ cup buttermilk
- 5 tablespoons freshly squeezed lemon juice, divided
- 1 clove garlic, grated
- 2 tablespoons shallot, minced
- Salt and pepper to taste
- 2 tablespoons avocado oil, divided
- 1 ¼ cups quinoa, cooked
- 2 heads endive, sliced
- 2 firm pears, sliced thinly
- 2 avocados, sliced
- ¼ cup fresh dill, chopped

Direction

1. Combine the vinegar, cream, milk, 1 tablespoon lemon juice, garlic, shallot, salt and pepper in a bowl.
2. Pour 1 tablespoon oil into a pan over medium heat.

3. Heat the quinoa for 4 minutes.

4. Transfer quinoa to a plate.

5. Toss the endive and pears in a mixture of remaining oil, remaining lemon juice, salt and pepper.

6. Transfer to a plate.

7. Toss the avocado in the reserved dressing.

8. Add to the plate.

9. Top with the dill and quinoa.

Nutrition

- Calories: 431
- Total fat: 28.5g
- Saturated fat: 8g
- Cholesterol: 13mg

Roasted Sweet Potatoes

Preparation Time: 20 minutes

Cooking Time: 20 minutes

Servings: 4

Ingredients:

- 2 potatoes, sliced into wedges
- 2 tablespoons olive oil, divided
- Salt and pepper to taste
- 1 red bell pepper, chopped
- ¼ cup fresh cilantro, chopped
- 1 garlic, minced
- 2 tablespoons almonds, toasted and sliced
- 1 tablespoon lime juice

Direction:

1. Preheat your oven to 425 degrees F.
2. Toss the sweet potatoes in oil and salt.
3. Transfer to a baking pan.
4. Roast for 20 minutes.

5. In a bowl, combine the red bell pepper, cilantro, garlic and almonds.

6. In another bowl, mix the lime juice, remaining oil, salt and pepper.

7. Drizzle this mixture over the red bell pepper mixture.

8. Serve sweet potatoes with the red bell pepper mixture.

Nutrition

- Calories: 146
- Total fat: 8.6g
- Saturated fat: 1.1g
- Sodium: 317mg

Cauliflower Salad

Preparation Time: 20 minutes

Cooking Time: 15 minutes

Servings: 4

Ingredients:

- 8 cups cauliflower florets
- 5 tablespoons olive oil, divided
- Salt and pepper to taste
- 1 cup parsley
- 1 clove garlic, minced
- 2 tablespoons lemon juice
- ¼ cup almonds, toasted and sliced
- 3 cups arugula
- 2 tablespoons olives, sliced
- ¼ cup feta, crumbled

Direction

1. Preheat your oven to 425 degrees F.
2. Toss the cauliflower in a mixture of 1 tablespoon olive oil, salt and pepper.

3. Place in a baking pan and roast for 15 minutes.
4. Put the parsley, remaining oil, garlic, lemon juice, salt and pepper in a blender.
5. Pulse until smooth.
6. Place the roasted cauliflower in a salad bowl.
7. Stir in the rest of the ingredients along with the parsley dressing.

Nutrition

- Calories: 198
- Total fat: 16.5g
- Saturated fat: 3g
- Cholesterol: 6mg

Garlic Mashed Potatoes & Turnips

Preparation Time: 20 minutes

Cooking Time: 30 minutes

Servings: 8

Ingredients:

- 1 head garlic
- 1 teaspoon olive oil
- 1 lb. turnips, sliced into cubes
- 2 lb. potatoes, sliced into cubes
- ½ cup almond milk
- ½ cup Parmesan cheese, grated
- 1 tablespoon fresh thyme, chopped
- 1 tablespoon fresh chives, chopped
- 2 tablespoons butter
- Salt and pepper to taste

Direction:

1. Preheat your oven to 375 degrees F.

2. Slice the tip off the garlic head.

3. Drizzle with a little oil and roast in the oven for 45 minutes.

4. Boil the turnips and potatoes in a pot of water for 30 minutes or until tender.

5. Add all the ingredients to a food processor along with the garlic.

6. Pulse until smooth.

Nutrition

- Calories: 141
- Total fat: 3.2g
- Saturated fat: 1.5g
- Cholesterol: 7mg

Cashew Siam Salad

Preparation Time: 10 minutes

Cooking Time:: 3 minutes

Servings: 4

Ingredients:

Salad:

- 4 cups baby spinach, rinsed, drained
- ½ cup pickled red cabbage

Dressing:

- 1-inch piece ginger, finely chopped
- 1 tsp. chili garlic paste
- 1 tbsp. soy sauce
- ½ tbsp. rice vinegar
- 1 tbsp. sesame oil
- 3 tbsp. avocado oil

Toppings:

- ½ cup raw cashews, unsalted
- ¼ cup fresh cilantro, chopped

Directions:

1.Put the spinach and red cabbage in a large bowl. Toss to combine and set the salad aside.

2.Toast the cashews in a frying pan over medium-high heat, stirring occasionally until the cashews are golden brown. This should take about 3 minutes. Turn off the heat and set the frying pan aside.

3.Mix all the dressing ingredients in a medium-sized bowl and use a spoon to mix them into a smooth dressing.

4.Pour the dressing over the spinach salad and top with the toasted cashews.

5.Toss the salad to combine all ingredients and transfer the large bowl to the fridge. Allow the salad to chill for up to one hour – doing so will guarantee a better flavor. Alternatively, the salad can be served right away, topped with the optional cilantro. Enjoy!

Nutrition:

- Calories 236
- Carbohydrates 6.1 g

- Fats 21.6 g
- Protein 4.2 g

Avocado and Cauliflower Hummus

Preparation Time: 5 minutes

Cooking Time:: 25 minutes

Servings: 2

Ingredients:

- 1 medium cauliflower, stem removed and chopped
- 1 large Hass avocado, peeled, pitted, and chopped
- ¼ cup extra virgin olive oil
- 2 garlic cloves
- ½ tbsp. lemon juice
- ½ tsp. onion powder
- Sea salt and ground black pepper to taste
- 2 large carrots
- ¼ cup fresh cilantro, chopped

Directions:

1.Preheat the oven to 450°F, and line a baking tray with aluminum foil.

2.Put the chopped cauliflower on the baking tray and drizzle with 2 tablespoons of olive oil.

3.Roast the chopped cauliflower in the oven for 20-25 minutes, until lightly brown.

4.Remove the tray from the oven and allow the cauliflower to cool down.

5.Add all the ingredients—except the carrots and

optional fresh cilantro—to a food processor or blender, and blend the ingredients into a smooth hummus.

6.Transfer the hummus to a medium-sized bowl, cover, and put it in the fridge for at least 30 minutes.

7.Take the hummus out of the fridge and, if desired, top it with the optional chopped cilantro and more salt and pepper to taste; serve with the carrot fries, and enjoy!

Nutrition:

- Calories 416
- Carbohydrates 8.4 g
- Fats 40.3 g
- Protein 3.3 g

Raw Zoodles with Avocado 'N Nuts

Preparation Time: 10 minutes

Servings: 2

Ingredients:

- 1 medium zucchini
- 1½ cups basil
- 1/3 cup water
- 5 tbsp. pine nuts
- 2 tbsp. lemon juice
- 1 medium avocado, peeled, pitted, sliced
- Optional: 2 tbsp. olive oil
- 6 yellow cherry tomatoes, halved
- Optional: 6 red cherry tomatoes, halved
- Sea salt and black pepper to taste

Directions:

1.Add the basil, water, nuts, lemon juice, avocado slices, optional olive oil (if desired), salt, and pepper to a blender.

2.Blend the ingredients into a smooth mixture. Add more salt and pepper to taste and blend again.

3.Divide the sauce and the zucchini noodles between two medium-sized bowls for serving, and combine in each.

4.Top the mixtures with the halved yellow cherry tomatoes, and the optional red cherry tomatoes (if desired); serve and enjoy!

Nutrition:

- Calories 317
- Carbohydrates 7.4 g
- Fats 28.1 g
- Protein 7.2 g

Cauliflower Sushi

Preparation Time: 30 minutes

Servings: 4

Ingredients:

Sushi Base:

- 6 cups cauliflower florets
- ½ cup vegan cheese
- 1 medium spring onion, diced
- 4 nori sheets
- Sea salt and pepper to taste
- 1 tbsp. rice vinegar or sushi vinegar
- 1 medium garlic clove, minced

Filling:

- 1 medium Hass avocado, peeled, sliced
- ½ medium cucumber, skinned, sliced
- 4 asparagus spears
- A handful of enoki mushrooms

Directions:

1.Put the cauliflower florets in a food processor or

blender. Pulse the florets into a rice-like substance. When using readymade cauliflower rice, add this to the blender.

2.Add the vegan cheese, spring onions, and vinegar to the food processor or blender. Top these ingredients with salt and pepper to taste, and pulse everything into a chunky mixture. Make sure not to turn the ingredients into a puree by pulsing too long.

3.Taste and add more vinegar, salt, or pepper to taste. Add the optional minced garlic clove to the blender and pulse again for a few seconds.

4.Lay out the nori sheets and spread the cauliflower rice mixture out evenly between the sheets. Make sure to leave at least 2 inches of the top and bottom edges empty.

5.Place one or more combinations of multiple filling ingredients along the center of the spread out rice mixture. Experiment with different ingredients per nori sheet for the best flavor.

6.Roll up each nori sheet tightly. (Using a sushi mat will make this easier.)

7.Either serve the sushi as a nori roll, or, slice each roll up into sushi pieces.

8.Serve right away with a small amount of wasabi, pickled ginger, and soy sauce!

Nutrition:

- Calories 189
- Carbohydrates 7.6 g
- Fats 14.4 g
- Protein 6.1 g

Spinach and Mashed Tofu Salad

Preparation Time: 20 minutes

Cooking Time: 15 minutes

Servings: 4

Ingredients:

- 2 8-oz. blocks firm tofu, drained
- 4 cups baby spinach leaves
- 4 tbsp. cashew butter
- 1½ tbsp. soy sauce

- 1-inch piece ginger, finely chopped
- 1 tsp. red miso paste
- 2 tbsp. sesame seeds
- 1 tsp. organic orange zest
- 1 tsp. nori flakes
- 2 tbsp. water

Directions:

1.Use paper towels to absorb any excess water left in the tofu before crumbling both blocks into small pieces.

2.In a large bowl, combine the mashed tofu with the spinach leaves.

3.Mix the remaining ingredients in another small bowl and, if desired, add the optional water for a more smooth dressing.

4.Pour this dressing over the mashed tofu and spinach leaves.

5.Transfer the bowl to the fridge and allow the salad to chill for up to one hour. Doing so will guarantee a better flavor. Or, the salad can be served right away. Enjoy!

Nutrition:

- Calories 166
- Carbohydrates 5.5 g
- Fats 10.7 g
- Protein 11.3 g

Cucumber Edamame Salad

Preparation Time: 5 minutes

Cooking Time:: 8 minutes

Servings: 2

Ingredients:

- 3 tbsp. avocado oil
- 1 cup cucumber, sliced into thin rounds
- ½ cup fresh sugar snap peas, sliced or whole
- ½ cup fresh edamame
- ¼ cup radish, sliced
- 1 large Hass avocado, peeled, pitted, sliced
- 1 nori sheet, crumbled
- 2 tsp. roasted sesame seeds
- 1 tsp. salt

Directions:

1.Bring a medium-sized pot filled halfway with water to a boil over medium-high heat.

2.Add the sugar snaps and cook them for about 2

minutes.

3.Take the pot off the heat, drain the excess water, transfer the sugar snaps to a medium-sized bowl and set aside for now.

4.Fill the pot with water again, add the teaspoon of salt and bring to a boil over medium-high heat.

5.Add the edamame to the pot and let them cook for about 6 minutes.

6.Take the pot off the heat, drain the excess water, transfer the soybeans to the bowl with sugar snaps and let them cool down for about 5 minutes.

7.Combine all ingredients, except the nori crumbs and roasted sesame seeds, in a medium-sized bowl.

8.Carefully stir, using a spoon, until all ingredients are evenly coated in oil.

9.Top the salad with the nori crumbs and roasted sesame seeds.

10.Transfer the bowl to the fridge and allow the salad to cool for at least 30 minutes.

11. Serve chilled and enjoy!

Nutrition:

- Calories 409

- Carbohydrates 7.1 g
- Fats 38.25 g
- Protein 7.6 g

Artichoke White Bean Sandwich Spread

Preparation Time: 10 minutes

Cooking Time: 15 minutes

Servings: 2

Ingredients:

- ½ cup raw cashews, chopped
- Water
- 1 clove garlic, cut into half

- 1 tablespoon lemon zest
- 1 teaspoon fresh rosemary, chopped
- ¼ teaspoon salt
- ¼ teaspoon pepper
- 6 tablespoons almond, soy or coconut milk
- 1 15.5-ounce can cannellini beans, rinsed and drained well
- 3 to 4 canned artichoke hearts, chopped
- ¼ cup hulled sunflower seeds
- Green onions, chopped, for garnish

Directions:

1.Soak the raw cashews for 15 minutes in enough water to cover them. Drain and dab with a paper towel to make them as dry as possible.

2.Transfer the cashews to a blender and add the garlic, lemon zest, rosemary, salt and pepper. Pulse to break everything up and then add the milk, one tablespoon at a time, until the mixture is smooth and creamy.

3.Mash the beans in a bowl with a fork. Add the artichoke hearts and sunflower seeds. Toss to mix.

4.Pour the cashew mixture on top and season with

more salt and pepper if desired. Mix the ingredients well and spread on whole-wheat bread, crackers, or a wrap.

Nutrition:

- Calories 110
- Carbohydrates 14 g
- Fats 4 g
- Protein 6 g

Dinner

Curried Tofu with Buttery Cabbage

Preparation Time: 15 minutes

Cooking Time: 10 minutes

Servings: 4

Ingredients

- 2 cups extra-firm tofu, pressed and cubed
- 1 tbsp + 3 ½ tbsp coconut oil
- ½ cup unsweetened shredded coconut
- 1 tsp yellow curry powder
- 1 tsp salt
- ½ tsp onion powder
- 2 cups Napa cabbage
- 4 oz. vegan butter
- Salt and black pepper to taste
- Lemon wedges for serving

Directions

1. In a medium bowl, add the tofu, 1 tablespoon of coconut oil, curry powder, salt, and onion powder. Mix well until the tofu is well-coated with the spices.

2. Heat the remaining coconut oil in a non-stick skillet and fry the tofu until golden brown on all sides, 8 minutes. Divide onto serving plates and set aside for serving.

3. In another skillet, melt half of the vegan butter, and sauté the cabbage until slightly caramelized, 2 minutes. Season with salt, black pepper, and plate to the side of the tofu.

4. Melt the remaining vegan butter in the skillet and drizzle all over the cabbage. Serve warm.

Nutrition

- calories 270
- fat 15
- fiber 3
- carbs 5
- protein 9

Smoked Tempeh with Broccoli Fritters

Preparation Time: 25 minutes

Cooking Time: 20 minutes

Servings: 4

Ingredients:

For the flax egg:

4 tbsp flax seed powder + 12 tbsp water

For the grilled tempeh:

- 3 tbsp olive oil
- 1 tbsp soy sauce
- 3 tbsp fresh lime juice
- 1 tbsp grated ginger
- Salt and cayenne pepper to taste
- 10 oz. tempeh slices

For the broccoli fritters:
- 2 cups of rice broccoli
- 8 oz. tofu cheese
- 3 tbsp plain flour
- ½ tsp onion powder
- 1 tsp salt
- ¼ tsp freshly ground black pepper
- 4¼ oz. vegan butter

For serving:
- ½ cup mixed salad greens
- 1 cup vegan mayonnaise
- ½ lemon, juiced

Directions:

1. For the smoked tempeh:

2. In a bowl, mix the flax seed powder with water and set aside to soak for 5 minutes.

3. In another bowl, combine the olive oil, soy sauce, lime juice, grated ginger, salt, and cayenne pepper. Brush the tempeh slices with the mixture.

4. Heat a grill pan over medium heat and grill the tempeh on both sides until nicely smoked and golden brown, 8 minutes. Transfer to a plate and set aside in a warmer for serving.

5. In a medium bowl, combine the broccoli rice, tofu cheese, flour, onion, salt, and black pepper. Mix in the flax egg until well combine and form 1-inch thick patties out of the mixture.

6. Melt the vegan butter in a medium skillet over medium heat and fry the patties on both sides until golden brown, 8 minutes. Remove the fritters onto a plate and set aside.

7. In a small bowl, mix the vegan mayonnaise with the lemon juice.

8. Divide the smoked tempeh and broccoli fritters onto serving plates, add the salad greens, and serve with the vegan mayonnaise sauce.

Nutrition

- Calories; 21g
- Fat; 4.7g
- Carbs; 44.2g
- Protein; 0
- 0.5g Sugars

Cheesy Potato Casserole

Preparation Time: 30 minutes

Cooking Time: 20 minutes

Servings: 4

Ingredients:

- 2 oz. vegan butter
- ½ cup celery stalks, finely chopped
- 1 white onion, finely chopped
- 1 green bell pepper, seeded and finely chopped
- Salt and black pepper to taste
- 2 cups peeled and chopped potatoes
- 1 cup vegan mayonnaise
- 4 oz. freshly shredded vegan Parmesan cheese
- 1 tsp red chili flakes

Directions:

1. Preheat the oven to 400 F and grease a baking dish with cooking spray.

2. Season the celery, onion, and bell pepper with salt and black pepper.
3. In a bowl, mix the potatoes, vegan mayonnaise, Parmesan cheese, and red chili flakes.
4. Pour the mixture into the baking dish, add the season vegetables, and mix well.
5. Bake in the oven until golden brown, about 20 minutes.
6. Remove the baked potato and serve warm with baby spinach.

Nutrition
- calories 277
- fat 17
- fiber 5
- carbs 8
- protein 10

Curry Mushroom Pie

Preparation Time: 65 minutes

Cooking Time: 1 hour

Servings: 4

Ingredients:

For the piecrust:

- 1 tbsp flax seed powder + 3 tbsp water
- ¾ cup plain flour
- 4 tbsp. chia seeds
- 4 tbsp almond flour
- 1 tbsp nutritional yeast
- 1 tsp baking powder
- 1 pinch salt
- 3 tbsp olive oil
- 4 tbsp water

For the filling:

- 1 cup chopped baby Bella mushrooms
- 1 cup vegan mayonnaise

- 3 tbsp + 9 tbsp water
- ½ red bell pepper, finely chopped
- 1 tsp curry powder
- ½ tsp paprika powder
- ½ tsp garlic powder
- ¼ tsp black pepper
- ½ cup coconut cream
- 1¼ cups shredded vegan Parmesan cheese

Directions:

1. In two separate bowls, mix the different portions of flaxseed powder with the respective quantity of water. Allow soaking for 5 minutes.
2. For the piecrust:
3. Preheat the oven to 350 F.
4. When the flax egg is ready, pour the smaller quantity into a food processor and pour in all the ingredients for the piecrust. Blend until soft, smooth dough forms.
5. Line an 8-inch springform pan with parchment paper and grease with cooking spray.
6. Spread the dough in the bottom of the pan and bake for 15 minutes.

7. For the filling:

8. In a bowl, add the remaining flax egg and all the filling's ingredients. Combine well and pour the mixture on the piecrust. Bake further for 40 minutes or until the pie is golden brown.

9. Remove from the oven and allow cooling for 1 minute.

10.   Slice and serve the pie warm.

Nutrition

- Calories 210
- Fat 3.7g
- Carbs 49.2g
- Protein 0.5g

Spicy Cheesy Tofu Balls

Preparation Time: 30 minutes

Cooking Time: 15 minutes

Servings: 4

Ingredients:

- 1/3 cup vegan mayonnaise
- ¼ cup pickled jalapenos
- 1 pinch cayenne pepper
- 4 oz. grated vegan cheddar cheese
- 1 tsp paprika powder
- 1 tbsp mustard powder
- 1 tbsp flax seed powder + 3 tbsp water
- 2 ½ cup crumbled tofu
- Salt and black pepper to taste
- 2 tbsp vegan butter, for frying

Directions:

1. For the spicy cheese:

2. In a bowl, mix all the ingredients for the spicy vegan cheese until well combined. Set aside.
3. In another medium bowl, combine the flax seed powder with water and allow soaking for 5 minutes.
4. Add the flax egg to the cheese mixture, the crumbled tofu, salt, and black pepper, and combine well. Use your hands to form large meatballs out of the mix.
5. Melt the vegan butter in a large skillet over medium heat and fry the tofu balls until cooked and golden brown on all sides, 10 minutes.
6. Serve the tofu balls with your favorite mashes or in burgers.

Nutrition
- Calories 280
- Fat 3,8g
- Carbs 44.6g
- Protein 0.7g

Greek-style Gigante Beans

Preparation Time: 8 hours 5 minutes

Cooking Time:: 10 hours

Servings: 10

Ingredients:

- 12 ounces gigante beans
- 1 can tomatoes with juice, chopped
- 2 stalks celery, diced
- 1 onion, diced
- 4 garlic cloves, minced
- Salt, to taste

Directions:

1.Soak beans in water for 8 hours.

2.Combine drained beans with the remaining ingredients. Stir, and pour water to cover.

3.Cook for 10 hours on low. Season with salt, and serve.

Nutrition:

- Calories 63
- Carbohydrates 13 g
- Fats 2 g
- Protein 4 g

Brown Rice & Red Beans & Coconut Milk

Preparation Time: 10 minutes

Cooking Time:: 1 hour

Servings: 6

Ingredients:

- 2 cups brown rice, uncooked
- 4 cups water
- 1 Tbsp olive oil
- 1 onion, diced
- 3 cloves garlic, minced
- 2 cans red beans
- 1 can coconut milk

Directions:

1.Bring brown rice in water to a boil, then simmer for 30 minutes.

2.Sauté onion in olive oil. Add garlic and cook until golden.

3.Mix the onions and garlic, beans, and coconut milk into the rice. Simmer for 15 minutes.

4.Serve hot.

Nutrition:

- Calories 280
- Carbohydrates 49 g
- Fats 3 g
- Protein 8 g

Black-Eyed Peas with Herns

Preparation Time: 10 minutes

Cooking Time:: 1 hour

Servings: 8

Ingredients:

- 2 cans no-sodium black-eyed beans
- ½ cup extra-virgin olive oil
- 1 cup parsley, chopped
- 4 green onions, sliced
- 2 carrots, grated
- 2 Tbsp tomato paste
- 2 cups water
- Salt, pepper, to taste

Directions:

1. Drain the beans, reserve the liquid.
2. Sauté beans, parsley, onions, and carrots in oil for 3 minutes.

3.Add remaining ingredients, 2 cups reserved beans liquid, and water.

4.Cook for 30 minutes.

5.Season with salt, pepper and serve.

Nutrition:

- Calories 230
- Carbohydrates 23 g
- Fats 15 g
- Protein 11 g

Cream of Mushroom Soup

Preparation time: 5 minutes

Cooking time: 12 minutes

Servings: 6

Ingredients:

- 1 medium white onion, peeled, chopped
- 16 ounces button mushrooms, sliced
- 1 ½ teaspoon minced garlic
- 1/4 cup all-purpose flour
- 1/2 teaspoon ground black pepper
- 1 teaspoon dried thyme
- 1/4 teaspoon nutmeg
- 1/2 teaspoon salt
- 2 tablespoons vegan butter
- 4 cups vegetable broth
- 1 1/2 cups coconut milk, unsweetened

Directions:

1.Take a large pot, place it over medium-high heat, add butter and when it melts, add onions and garlic, stir in garlic and cook for 5 minutes until softened and nicely brown.

2.Then sprinkle flour over vegetables, continue cooking for 1 minute, then add remaining ingredients, stir until mixed and simmer for 5 minutes until thickened.

3.Serve straight away

Nutrition:

- Calories: 120 Cal
- Fat: 7 g
- Carbs: 10 g
- Protein: 2 g
- Fiber: 6 g

Cauliflower and Horseradish Soup

Preparation time: 5 minutes

Cooking time: 20 minutes

Servings: 4

Ingredients:

- 2 medium potatoes, peeled, chopped
- 1 medium cauliflower, florets and stalk chopped
- 1 medium white onion, peeled, chopped
- 1 teaspoon minced garlic
- 2/3 teaspoon salt
- 1/3 teaspoon ground black pepper
- 4 teaspoons horseradish sauce
- 1 teaspoon dried thyme
- 3 cups vegetable broth
- 1 cup coconut milk, unsweetened

Directions:

1.Place all the vegetables in a large pan, place it over

medium-high heat, add thyme, pour in broth and milk and bring the mixture to boil.

2.Then switch heat to medium level, simmer the soup for 15 minutes and remove the pan from heat.

3.Puree the soup by using an immersion blender until smooth, season with salt and black pepper, and serve straight away.

Nutrition:

- Calories: 160 Cal
- Fat: 2.6 g
- Carbs: 31 g
- Protein: 6 g
- Fiber: 6 g

Curry Lentil Soup

Preparation time: 5 minutes

Cooking time: 40 minutes

Servings: 6

Ingredients:

1. 1 cup brown lentils
2. 1 medium white onion, peeled, chopped
3. 28 ounces diced tomatoes
4. 1 ½ teaspoon minced garlic
5. 1 inch of ginger, grated
6. 3 cups vegetable broth
7. 1/2 teaspoon salt
8. 2 tablespoons curry powder
9. 1 teaspoon cumin
10. 1/2 teaspoon cayenne
11. 1 tablespoon olive oil
12. 1 1/2 cups coconut milk, unsweetened
13. ¼ cup chopped cilantro
14.

Directions:

1.Take a soup pot, place it over medium-high heat, add oil and when hot, add onion, stir in garlic and ginger and cook for 5 minutes until golden brown.

2.Then add all the ingredients except for milk and cilantro, stir until mixed and simmer for 25 minutes until lentils have cooked.

3.When done, stir in milk, cook for 5 minutes until thoroughly heated and then garnish the soup with cilantro.

4.Serve straight away

Nutrition:

- Calories: 269 Cal
- Fat: 15 g
- Carbs: 26 g
- Protein: 10 g
- Fiber: 10 g

Chickpea Noodle Soup

Preparation time: 5 minutes

Cooking time: 18 minutes

Servings: 6

Ingredients:

- 1 cup cooked chickpeas
- 8 ounces rotini noodles, whole-wheat

- 4 celery stalks, sliced
- 2 medium white onions, peeled, chopped
- 4 medium carrots, peeled, sliced
- 2 teaspoons minced garlic
- 8 sprigs of thyme
- 1 teaspoon salt
- 1/3 teaspoon ground black pepper
- 1 bay leaf
- 2 tablespoons olive oil
- 2 quarts of vegetable broth
- ¼ cup chopped fresh parsley

Directions:

1.Take a large pot, place it over medium heat, add oil and when hot, add all the vegetables, stir in garlic, thyme and bay leaf and cook for 5 minutes until vegetables are golden and sauté.

2.Then pour in broth stir and bring the mixture to boil.

3.Add chickpeas and noodles into boiling soup, continue cooking for 8 minutes until noodles are tender, and then season soup with salt and black pepper.

4.Garnish with parsley and serve straight away

Nutrition:

- Calories: 260 Cal
- Fat: 5 g
- Carbs: 44 g
- Protein: 7 g
- Fiber: 4 g

Ketogenic and Intermittent Fasting Diet

A New Complete Diet Guide for Vegetarians, with Intermittent Fasting Strategy, to lose weight and Fast Fat Burning. With delicious recipes for snacks and desserts.

Sebi Alan Guntry

Introduction

A keto diet for vegetarians is focused on proportionately eating more foods primarily from plants and cutting back on animal-derived foods. However, it does not necessarily involve eliminating entire food groups and lean sources of protein. This means, those on a plant-based diet may still opt to eat some meat.

Going vegan, on the other hand, means being strictly against animal products in any form—from never eating meat and dairy products to not patronizing products tested on animals and not wearing animal products such as leather.

A healthy keto plant-based diet generally emphasizes meeting your nutritional needs by eating more whole plant foods, while reducing the intake of animal products. Whole foods refer to natural, unrefined or minimally refined foods. Plant foods consist of those that do not have animal ingredients such as meat, eggs, honey, milk and other dairy products.

In contrast, those on a vegetarian diet may still eat processed and refined foods. Vegetarians can even eat fast foods, junk food and other salty snacks guilt-free. Once you get started with this diet, you will notice a huge difference in how you feel each day. From the time that you wake up in the morning, you will feel that you have more energy, and that you do not get tired as easily as before. You will also have more mental focus and fewer mood-related problems.

As for digestion, a plant-based diet is also said to improve how the digestive system works. In fact, dieters confirm fewer incidences of stomach pains, bloating, indigestion and hyperacidity.

Then there's the weight loss benefit that we cannot forget about. Since a keto plant-based diet means eating fruits, vegetables, and whole grains that have fewer calories and are lower in fat, you will enjoy weight loss benefits that some other fad diets are not able to provide.

Aside from helping you lose weight; it maintains ideal weight longer because this diet is easier to sustain and does not require elimination of certain food groups.

Don't worry about not getting enough nutrients from your food intake. This diet provides all the necessary nutrients including proteins, vitamins, minerals, carbohydrates, fats, and antioxidants. And again, that's because it does not eliminate any food group but only encourages you to focus more on keto plant-based food products.

As you can imagine, humans have been consuming a keto plant-based diet before the invention of McDonald's and some of our other favorite fast-food chains. To begin our journey, I am going to start us off in the times of the hunter-gatherer. While we could go back even further (think Ancient Egypt!), I believe this is where a keto plant-based diet becomes most relevant.

The hunter-gatherer time period is where we find the earliest evidence of hunting. While we do have a long history of eating meat, this was a point in time where consuming meat was very limited. Of course, humans eating meat does not mean we were carnivores; in fact, the way we are built tells us differently. Yes, we can consume meat, but humans are considered omnivores. You can tell this from our jaw design, running speeds, alimentary tract, and the fact we don't have claws attached to our fingers. History also tells us we are omnivores by nature; however, the evolution of our human brains led us to become hunters so that we could survive.

The need for hunting did not come around until our ancestors left tropical regions. Other locations influenced the availability of keto plant-based foods. Instead of enduring winter with limited amounts of food, we had to adapt! Of course, out of hunger, animal-flesh becomes much more appealing. This early in time, our ancestors did not have a grocery store to just pop in and buy whatever they needed. Instead, they used the opportunity of hunting and gathering to keep themselves alive.

Eventually, we moved away from hunting and gathering and started to become farmers. While this timeline is a bit tricky and agricultural history began at different points in different parts of the world, all that matters is that at some point; animals started to become domesticated and dairy, eggs, and meat all became readily available. Once this started, humans no longer needed to hunt nor gather because the farmers provided everything we could desire

While starting a keto plant-based diet is an excellent idea and has many wonderful benefits let's be honest, you are mostly here to benefit yourself. It is fantastic that you are deciding to put you and your health first. You deserve to be the best version of yourself, with a little bit of legwork, you will be there in no time

To some people, a keto plant-based diet is just another fad diet. There are so many diets on the market right now, why is plant-based any different? Whether you are looking to lose weight, reverse disease, or just love animals.

A plant-based diet is so much more than just eating fruits and vegetables. This is a lifestyle where you are encouraged to journey to a better version of yourself. As you improve your eating habits, you will need something to do with all of your new found energy! It is time to gain control over your eating habits and figure out how food truly does affect our daily lives! Below, you will find the amazing benefits a plant-based diet has to offer you.

The Circadian Cycle

The circadian cycle is nothing more than the set of variations to which our biological activities are subjected on a daily basis:

- Blood pressure
- Body temperature
- Muscle tone
- Heart rate

- Sleep-wake rhythm
- Lipid metabolism

It is of fundamental importance to know our circadian rhythm because depending on the phases of our body needs certain foods and not others.

Foods according to the phases of the cycle:

- between 7 a.m. - 3 p.m. it would be better to take carbohydrates
- between 3 pm and 8 pm is the protein phase

Snacks For Morning And Afternoon

Strawberry Mango Shave Ice

Preparation time: 20 minutes

Cooking time: 10 minutes

Serving: 4

Ingredients:

½ cup superfine sugar, divided

1-cup strawberries, diced

2 diced mangos

2 cups mango juice

½ cup coconut, toasted

Directions:

Add 1 cup water and ¾ cup sugar to a pot and boil over medium heat.

Once boiled, remove from heat and add 2 more cups of water.

Freeze this mixture stirring after every 45 minutes.

Take a blender and add all remaining ingredients and blend until smooth.

Strain the mixture into a container with a pour spout.

For serving, divide the ice into glasses and pour juice and mixture over them.

Serve and enjoy.

Nutrition:

Calories 366

Fat 5.5 g,

Carbs 82.4 g,

Protein 2.7 g

Banana Muffins

Preparation time: 10 minutes

Cooking time: 15 minutes

Serving: 6

Ingredients:

- 1 cup rolled oats
- 1 medium banana
- 2 tablespoons ground flaxseed
- 1/4 teaspoon sea salt
- 3/4 teaspoon baking powder
- 1/4 teaspoon baking soda
- 3 tablespoons vanilla protein powder

- 1/2 teaspoon vanilla extract. unsweetened
- 2 tablespoons maple syrup
- 5 tablespoons water
- 2/3 cup soy yogurt, unsweetened

Directions:

1. Prepare the flax egg and for this, take a large bowl, place ground flaxseed, stir in water and let it stand for 5 minutes until thickened.
2. Switch on the oven, then set it to 400 degrees F and let it preheat.
3. After 5 minutes, add remaining ingredients into the flax egg and then mix with an electric mixer until incorporated and smooth batter comes together.
4. Take five silicone muffin cups, fill them evenly with batter and then bake for 15 minutes until golden brown.
5. When done, let muffins cool for 10 minutes on a wire rack and then serve.

Nutrition

- Calories 398
- Fat 3.8g

- Carbs 44.2g
- Protein 15g

Chocolate Protein Power Bars

Preparation time: 3 hours

Cooking time: 40 minutes

Serving: 6

Ingredients:

For the Filling:

- 2 cups of quick oats
- 8 Medjool dates pitted
- ¼ teaspoon salt

3½ tablespoons chocolate protein powder

1 teaspoon vanilla extract, unsweetened

2 tablespoons maple syrup

½ teaspoon almond extract, unsweetened

¼ cup of water

For the Coating:

¼ teaspoon almond extract, unsweetened

1¼ cups melted dark chocolate

1 tablespoon coconut oil

Directions:

Prepare the filling and for this, place all of its ingredients in a food processor and then pulse for 2 minutes until well incorporated.

Take a rectangular container, about 3 by 5 inches, place filling in it, then spread it evenly and freeze for a minimum of 3 hours until firm.

Along with the filling, take a small metal tray, line it with parchment paper, and let it chill in the freezer until required.

When ready to coat, take a shallow dish, place

melted chocolate in it, add dark chocolate and coconut oil and then stir until mixed.

Then remove the filling container from the container, transfer the filling block onto a cutting board, and cut it into six squares.

Working on one square at a time, dip it into melted chocolate, wipe the excess chocolate, place it on the chilled metal tray and repeat with the remaining square.

Return the metal tray into the freezer for 30 minutes until chocolate is hard and then serve.

Nutrition

Calories 398

Fat 4.8g

Carbs 49g

Protein 5g

Cherry and Berry Parfait

Preparation time: 8 hours

Cooking time: 5 minutes

Serving: 2

Ingredients:

- 1 cup granola
- 1/4 cup chia seeds
- 1 1/2 cup mixed berries
- 2 tablespoons honey
- 2 teaspoons vanilla extract, unsweetened
- 1 cup almond milk, unsweetened

Directions:

1. Take a large bowl, place chia seeds in it, add honey and vanilla, pour in milk, stir until combined and let it stand in the refrigerator overnight.

2. When ready to eat, stir the chia mixture, divide it evenly between two bowls, top it evenly with mixed berries and granola and then serve.

Nutrition

Calories; 21g

Fat; 4.7g

Carbs; 44.2g

Protein; 0

.5g Sugars

Brownie Batter Bites

Preparation time: 10 minutes

Cooking time: 5 minutes

Serving: 5

Ingredients:

10 tablespoons cocoa powder

4 tablespoons chocolate chips

1/4 teaspoon sea salt

2 teaspoons vanilla extract, unsweetened

6 tablespoons maple syrup

1/4 cup pea protein powder

1/4 cup almond butter

Directions:

Take a large bowl, add all the ingredients in it except for chocolate chips and then stir until well mixed.

Fold in chocolate chips, and then shape the mixture into ten balls, each about 2-inch in size.

Serve straight away.

Nutrition

Calories 248

Fat; 4.7g

Carbs; 44.2g

Protein; 0

.5g Sugars

Chocolate Chia Protein Pudding

Preparation time: 10 minutes

Cooking time: 30 minutes

Serving: 2

Ingredients:

4 tablespoons chia seeds

2 tablespoons vegan chocolate protein powder

2 tablespoons cocoa powder

1 tablespoon maple syrup

1 1/2 cup almond milk, unsweetened

Directions:

Place chia seeds in a food processor, add almond milk and then pulse for 30 seconds until blended.

Add remaining ingredients and then pulse for 1 minute until very smooth.

Distribute the pudding evenly between two bowls,

chill in the refrigerator for a minimum of 1 hour and then serve.

Nutrition:

- Calories 298
- Fat; 4.7g
- Carbs; 44.2g
- Protein 33 g

Chocolate Tofu Pudding

Preparation time: 1 hour

Cooking time: 20 minutes

Serving: 4

Ingredients

- 16 ounces silken tofu
- 1 tablespoon instant coffee
- 1/3 cup cacao powder
- 1/4 cup maple syrup
- 2 teaspoons vanilla extract, unsweetened

Directions

Place all the ingredients in the food processor in the order and then pulse at a high setting for 2 minutes until combined and very smooth.

Distribute the pudding among four bowls, chill in the refrigerator for a minimum of 1 hour and then serve.

Nutrition:

Calories 99

Fat; 4g

Carbs; 4g

Protein 50g

Chocolate Mousse

Preparation time: 1 hour

Cooking time: 0 minutes

Serving: 4

Ingredients

- 14 ounces silken tofu
- 1/2 cup chocolate, melted
- 2 tablespoons cacao powder, unsweetened
- 1/8 teaspoon salt
- 1/4 teaspoon ground cinnamon
- 4 tablespoons maple syrup
- 1/2 teaspoon vanilla extract, unsweetened
- 1/4 cup coconut cream

Directions:

Place all the ingredients in the food processor in the order and then pulse at a high setting for 2 minutes until combined and very smooth.

Distribute the mousse among four bowls, chill in the refrigerator for a minimum of 1 hour and then serve.

Nutrition:

Calories 98

Fat 4.7g

Carbs 4.2g

Protein 22 g

Sugars 2

Chocolate Black Bean and Orange Mousse

Preparation time: 1 hour

Cooking time: 5 minutes

Serving: 6

Ingredients:

- 15-ounce cooked black beans
- 1 orange, zested
- 1.7 ounces pitted dates
- 5 tablespoons cacao powder, unsweetened
- 1 teaspoon cacao nibs and more for topping
- 8 tablespoons maple syrup
- 2 tablespoons coconut oil, melted
- 4 tablespoons almond milk, unsweetened

Directions:

1. Place dates and black beans in a food processor and then pulse at a high setting for 1 minute.
2. Add remaining ingredients except for orange zest and pulse for 1 minute until blended.
3. Transfer the mousse into a bowl, add orange zest, and then stir until mixed.
4. Distribute the mousse among six bowls, sprinkle some more cacao nibs on top, and then chill in the refrigerator for a minimum of 1 hour.

5. Serve straight away.

Nutrition:

- Calories: 156
- Fat: 8.01g
- Carbohydrate: 20.33g
- Protein: 1.98g
- Sugar: 0.33g
- Cholesterol: 0mg

Carrot Cake Bites

Preparation time: 10 minutes

Cooking time: 0 minutes

Serving: 8

Ingredients:

1 cup chopped carrots

1 cup rolled oats

1/2 cup pecans

1/2 cup Medjool dates

1/2 teaspoon ground nutmeg

1 1/2 teaspoons ground cinnamon

1/4 cup cashew butter

1/2 cup coconut flakes

1/3 cup shredded coconut

Directions:

Place carrots in a food processor, then pulse for 2 minutes until finely chopped and transfer carrots into a large bowl.

Add coconut and pecans into the food processor, pulse for 1 minute until mixture resembles sand, then add dates and oats and blend for another mixture.

Add remaining ingredients except for coconut and then pulse for 2 minutes until the dough comes together.

Shape the dough into small balls, about 1 tablespoon of dough per ball, and then roll the balls into coconut until evenly coated.

Serve straight away.

Nutrition

Calories: 96

Fat: 8.8g

Carbohydrates: 5.12g

Protein: 1.2g

Sugar: 0.4g

Cholesterol: 0mg

Almond Milk

Preparation Time: 10-20 minutes

Cooking Time: 20 minutes plus overnight soaking

Servings: 500ml

Ingredients:

- Blanched almonds: 250g
- Maple syrup: 1 tsp

- Water: 500 ml

Directions:

Soaked almonds in the water overnight

Add maple syrup, blanched almonds, and water to the blender and blend till smoothen

Strain and discard the puree

Shake before serving

Nutrition:

Carbs: 1.3g

Protein: 1.4g

Fats: 2.9g

Calories: 35Kcal

Almond Roasted Veggies Salad

Preparation Time: 10-20 minutes

Cooking Time: 30 minutes

Servings: 4

Ingredients:

- Carrots: 1 cup sliced
- Broccoli: 1 cup sliced
- Cauliflower: 1 cup sliced
- Olive oil: 1 tbsp
- Salt: as per your taste

- Pepper: as per your taste
- Almonds: 1 cup whole roasted
- For the Dressing:
- Lemon: 2 zest and juice
- Mirin: 2 tbsp
- Garlic: 1 clove crushed
- Extra-virgin olive oil: 2 tbsp
- Salt: as per your need

Directions:

1. Add all the vegetables to the baking tray, sprinkle salt and pepper, brush with olive oil and bake for 20 minutes
2. Prepare the dressing by adding all the Ingredients: except oil and combine it slowly at the end whisking to gain the correct consistency
3. Add vegetables to the tray and pour dressing and almonds from the top and serve

Nutrition:

- Carbs: 11g
- Protein: 9.7g

- Fats: 25g
- Calories: 309Kcal

Apple Almond Mix

Preparation Time: 10-20 minutes

Cooking Time: 5 minutes

Servings: 4

Ingredients:

- Apple: 4 peeled and diced into bite-sized chunks
- Almond: 1 cup grated

- Lime: 1 juiced
- Sea salt: ½ tsp
- Coconut yogurt to serve

Directions:

- Place all the Ingredients: in a large bowl and shake them well
- Now serve it with some coconut yogurt if you desire

Nutrition:

- Carbs: 31g
- Protein: 7.5g
- Fats: 18.3g
- Calories: 395Kcal

Asian Cabbage Pickle

Preparation Time: 10-20 minutes

Cooking Time: 20 minutes plus marinating

Servings: 6

Ingredients:

- Red cabbage: 1 small
- Ginger: 4cm piece shredded
- Bird's-eye chilies: 2
- Caster sugar: 50g
- Vinegar: 100ml
- Sesame oil: 2 tsp
- Black sesame seeds: 2 tsp

Directions:

1. Take a cabbage
2. Remove the sagging outer leaves and quarter the cabbage
3. Remove the core and put the remaining in a bowl along with ginger and some slit chilies

4. Dissolved the sugar in the mixture of vinegar and sugar then pour 100 ml of water along with 1 teaspoon of salt
5. Marinate the cabbage for 2 hours
6. Take a bowl, drain the cabbage well and pour some sesame seeds and oil

Nutrition:

- Carbs: 5.9g
- Protein: 1.6g
- Fats: 1.7g
- Calories: 53Kcal

Avocado Chaat

Preparation Time: 10-20 minutes

Cooking Time: 5 minutes

Servings: 4

Ingredients:

- Avocado: 4 peeled and diced into bite-sized chunks
- Chaat masala: 2 tsp
- Lime: 1 juiced
- Sea salt: ½ tsp
- Coconut yogurt to serve

Directions:

Place all the Ingredients: in a large bowl and shake

them well

Now serve it with some coconut yogurt if you desire

Nutrition:

- Carbs:12 g
- Protein: 2.9g
- Fats: 21g
- Calories: 234Kcal

Avocado Potstickers

Preparation Time: 10-20 minutes

Cooking Time: 55 minutes

Servings: 36 potstickers

Ingredients:

Edamame: 1lb cooked (shelled)

Ripe avocado: 1 half reserved and one chopped

Bok choy: 1 small stem and leaves separated and diced

Ginger: 1 gm minced

Circle-shaped wonton wrappers: about 36 sheets

Garlic:3 cloves minced

Coconut sugar: 1½ tbsp

Scallions: 1 sliced

Ground white pepper:¼ tsp

Soy sauce: 2 tbsp

Chili sauce: 1 tbsp

Rice vinegar:½ tbsp

Toasted sesame oil: ½ tbsp

Directions:

Take a blender and add half avocado and three quarters of edamame and blend

Give them smooth consistency

Add the mixture to the bowl and add the remaining edamame, avocado, bok choy, green onions, garlic, ginger, and seasonings

Mix them all well

Line the baking sheet with parchment paper and place and wonton wrappers

Add the filling in the middle of the wrapper

Wet the wrapper corner and fold using fingers and do it

will all the wrappers

Bake till golden brown

Nutrition:

- Carbs: 18 g
- Protein: 7 g
- Fats: 3 g
- Calories: 123 Kcal

Avocado Peanut Salad

Preparation Time: 10-20 minutes

Cooking Time: 30 minutes

Servings: 4

Ingredients:

- Avocado: 2 cups diced
- Peanuts: ½ cup
- Lemon juice: 1 tbsp
- Mint: ¼ cup leaves torn
- For the Dressing:
- Vinegar: 2 tsp

- Garlic: 1 clove crushed
- Extra-virgin olive oil: 3 tbsp
- Tahini: 2 tbsp
- Lemon: 1 zest and juice
- Salt: as per your need

Directions:

1. Take a pan and add peanuts to roast them dry and crush using hand
2. Prepare the dressing by adding all the Ingredients: except oil and combine it slowly at the end whisking to gain the correct consistency
3. Add avocado to the serving tray
4. Top with peanuts
5. Sprinkle mint leaves and pour lemon juice and serve

Nutrition:

- Carbs: 11.4g
- Protein: 5.7g
- Fats: 34g
- Calories: 379Kcal

Desserts

Key Lime Pie

Preparation Time: 3 hours and 15 minutes

Cooking Time: 0 minute

Servings: 12

Ingredients:

For the Crust:

- ¾ cup coconut flakes, unsweetened
- 1 cup dates, soaked in warm water for 10 minutes in water, drained
- *For the Filling*:
- ¾ cup of coconut meat
- 1 ½ avocado, peeled, pitted
- 2 tablespoons key lime juice
- ¼ cup agave
-

Directions:

Prepare the crust, and for this, place all its ingredients in a food processor and pulse for 3 to 5 minutes until the thick paste comes together.

Take an 8-inch pie pan, grease it with oil, pour crust mixture in it and spread and press the mixture evenly in the bottom and along the sides, and freeze until required.

Prepare the filling and for this, place all its ingredients in a food processor, and pulse for 2 minutes until smooth.

Pour the filling into prepared pan, smooth the top, and freeze for 3 hours until set.

Cut pie into slices and then serve.

Nutrition:

Calories: 213 Cal

Fat: 10 g

Carbs: 29 g

Protein: 1200 g

Fiber: 6 g

Chocolate Mint Grasshopper Pie

Preparation Time: 4 hours and 15 minutes

Cooking Time: 0 minute

Servings: 4

Ingredients:

For the Crust:

- 1 cup dates, soaked in warm water for 10 minutes in water, drained
- 1/8 teaspoons salt
- 1/2 cup pecans
- 1 teaspoons cinnamon
- 1/2 cup walnuts

For the Filling:

- ½ cup mint leaves
- 2 cups of cashews, soaked in warm water for 10 minutes in water, drained
- 2 tablespoons coconut oil
- 1/4 cup and 2 tablespoons of agave

- 1/4 teaspoons spirulina
- 1/4 cup water

Directions:

1. Prepare the crust, and for this, place all its ingredients in a food processor and pulse for 3 to 5 minutes until the thick paste comes together.
2. Take a 6-inch springform pan, grease it with oil, place crust mixture in it and spread and press the mixture evenly in the bottom and along the sides, and freeze until required.
3. Prepare the filling and for this, place all its ingredients in a food processor, and pulse for 2 minutes until smooth.
4. Pour the filling into prepared pan, smooth the top, and freeze for 4 hours until set.
5. Cut pie into slices and then serve.

Nutrition:

- Calories: 223.7 Cal
- Fat: 7.5 g
- Carbs: 36 g
- Protein: 2.5 g
- Fiber: 1 g

Peanut Butter Energy Bars

Preparation Time: 5 hours and 15 minutes

Cooking Time: 5 minutes

Servings: 16

Ingredients:

- 1/2 cup cranberries
- 12 Medjool dates, pitted
- 1 cup roasted almond
- 1 tablespoon chia seeds
- 1 1/2 cups oats
- 1/8 teaspoon salt
- 1/4 cup and 1 tablespoon agave nectar
- 1/2 teaspoon vanilla extract, unsweetened
- 1/3 cup and 1 tablespoon peanut butter, unsalted
- 2 tablespoons water

Directions:

1. Place an almond in a food processor, pulse until chopped, and then transfer into a large bowl.

2. Add dates into the food processor along with oats, pour in water, and pulse for dates are chopped.

3. Add dates mixture into the almond mixture, add chia seeds and berries and stir until mixed.

4. Take a saucepan, place it over medium heat, add remaining butter and remaining ingredients, stir and cook for 5 minutes until mixture reaches to a liquid consistency.

5. Pour the butter mixture over date mixture, and then stir until well combined.

6. Take an 8 by 8 inches baking tray, line it with parchment sheet, add date mixture in it, spread and press it evenly and refrigerate for 5 hours.

7. Cut it into sixteen bars and serve.

Nutrition:

- Calories: 187 Cal
- Fat: 7.5 g
- Carbs: 27.2 g
- Protein: 4.7 g
- Fiber: 2 g

Black Bean Brownie Pops

Preparation Time: 45 minutes

Cooking Time: 2 minutes

Servings: 12

Ingredients:

- 3/4 cup chocolate chips
- 15 ounce cooked black beans
- 1 tablespoon maple syrup
- 5 tablespoons cacao powder
- 1/8 teaspoon sea salt
- 2 tablespoons sunflower seed butter

Directions:

1. Place black beans in a food processor, add remaining ingredients, except for chocolate, and pulse for 2 minutes until combined and the dough starts to come together.
2. Shape the dough into twelve balls, arrange them on a baking sheet lined with parchment paper,

then insert a toothpick into each ball and refrigerate for 20 minutes.

3. Then meat chocolate in the microwave for 2 minutes, and dip brownie pops in it until covered.

4. Return the pops into the refrigerator for 10 minutes until set and then serve.

Nutrition:

- Calories: 130 Cal
- Fat: 6 g
- Carbs: 17 g
- Protein: 4 g
- Fiber: 1 g

Lemon Cashew Tart

Preparation Time: 3 hours and 15 minutes

Cooking Time: 0 minute

Servings: 12

Ingredients:

For the Crust:

- 1 cup almonds
- 4 dates, pitted, soaked in warm water for 10 minutes in water, drained
- 1/8 teaspoon crystal salt
- 1 teaspoon vanilla extract, unsweetened

For the Cream:

- 1 cup cashews, soaked in warm water for 10 minutes in water, drained
- 1/4 cup water
- 1/4 cup coconut nectar
- 1 teaspoon coconut oil
- 1 teaspoon vanilla extract, unsweetened
- 1 lemon, Juiced
- 1/8 teaspoon crystal salt
- For the Topping:

- Shredded coconut as needed

Directions:

Prepare the cream and for this, place all its ingredients in a food processor, pulse for 2 minutes until smooth, and then refrigerate for 1 hour.

Then prepare the crust, and for this, place all its ingredients in a food processor and pulse for 3 to 5 minutes until the thick paste comes together.

Take a tart pan, grease it with oil, place crust mixture in it and spread and press the mixture evenly in the bottom and along the sides, and freeze until required.

Pour the filling into the prepared tart, smooth the top, and refrigerate for 2 hours until set.

Cut tart into slices and then serve.

Nutrition:

Calories: 166 Cal

Fat: 10 g

Carbs: 15 g

Protein: 5 g

Fiber: 1 g

Peppermint Oreos

Preparation Time: 2 hours

Cooking Time: 0 minute

Servings: 12

Ingredients:

For the Cookies:

- 1 cup dates
- 2/3 cup brazil nuts
- 3 tablespoons carob powder
- 2/3 cup almonds
- 1/8 teaspoon sea salt
- 3 tablespoons water

For the Crème:

- 2 tablespoons almond butter
- 1 cup coconut chips
- 2 tablespoons melted coconut oil
- 1 cup coconut shreds
- 3 drops of peppermint oil
- 1/2 teaspoon vanilla powder
- For the Dark Chocolate:

- 3/4 cup cacao powder
- 1/2 cup date paste
- 1/3 cup coconut oil, melted

Directions:

1. Prepare the cookies, and for this, place all its ingredients in a food processor and pulse for 3 to 5 minutes until the dough comes together.
2. Then place the dough between two parchment sheets, roll the dough, then cut out twenty-four cookies of the desired shape and freeze until solid.
3. Prepare the crème, and for this, place all its ingredients in a food processor and pulse for 2 minutes until smooth.
4. When cookies have hardened, sandwich crème in between the cookies by placing dollops on top of a cookie and then pressing it with another cookie.
5. Freeze the cookies for 30 minutes and in the meantime, prepare chocolate and for this, place all its ingredients in a bowl and whisk until combined.

6. Dip frouncesen cookie sandwich into chocolate, at least two times, and then freeze for another 30 minutes until chocolate has hardened.
7. Serve straight away.

Nutrition:

- Calories: 470 Cal
- Fat: 32 g
- Carbs: 51 g
- Protein: 7 g
- Fiber: 12 g

Snickers Pie

Preparation Time: 4 hours

Cooking Time: 0 minute

Servings: 16

Ingredients:

For the Crust:

- 12 Medjool dates, pitted
- 1 cup dried coconut, unsweetened
- 5 tablespoons cocoa powder
- 1/2 teaspoon sea salt
- 1 teaspoon vanilla extract, unsweetened
- 1 cup almonds

For the Caramel Layer:

- 10 Medjool dates, pitted, soaked for 10 minutes in warm water, drained
- 2 teaspoons vanilla extract, unsweetened
- 3 teaspoons coconut oil
- 3 tablespoons almond butter, unsalted
- *For the Peanut Butter Mousse:*

- 3/4 cup peanut butter
- 2 tablespoons maple syrup
- 1/2 teaspoon vanilla extract, unsweetened
- 1/8 teaspoon sea salt
- 28 ounces coconut milk, chilled

Directions:

1. Prepare the crust, and for this, place all its ingredients in a food processor and pulse for 3 to 5 minutes until the thick paste comes together.
2. Take a baking pan, line it with parchment paper, place crust mixture in it and spread and press the mixture evenly in the bottom, and freeze until required.
3. Prepare the caramel layer, and for this, place all its ingredients in a food processor and pulse for 2 minutes until smooth.
4. Pour the caramel on top of the prepared crust, smooth the top and freeze for 30 minutes until set.
5. Prepare the mousse and for this, separate coconut milk and its solid, then add solid from coconut milk into a food processor, add remaining

ingredients and then pulse for 1 minute until smooth.

6. Top prepared mousse over caramel layer, and then freeze for 3 hours until set.

7. Serve straight away.

Nutrition:

- Calories: 456 Cal
- Fat: 33 g
- Carbs: 37 g
- Protein: 8.3 g
- Fiber: 5 g

Double Chocolate Orange Cheesecake

Preparation Time: 4 hours

Cooking Time: 0 minute

Servings: 12

Ingredients:

For the Base:

- 9 Medjool dates, pitted
- 1/3 cup Brazil nuts
- 2 tablespoons maple syrup
- 1/3 cup walnuts
- 2 tablespoons water
- 3 tablespoons cacao powder

For the Chocolate Cheesecake:

- 1/2 cup cacao powder
- 1 1/2 cups cashews, soaked for 10 minutes in warm water, drained
- 1/3 cup liquid coconut oil
- 1 teaspoon vanilla extract, unsweetened

- 1/3 cup maple syrup
- 1/3 cup water

For the Orange Cheesecake:
- 2 oranges, juiced
- 1/4 cup maple syrup
- 1 cup cashews, soaked for 10 minutes in warm water, drained
- 1 teaspoon vanilla extract, unsweetened
- 2 tablespoons coconut butter
- 1/2 cup liquid coconut oil
- 2 oranges, zested
- 4 drops of orange essential oil

For the Chocolate Topping:
- 3 tablespoons cacao powder
- 3 drops of orange essential oil
- 2 tablespoons liquid coconut oil
- 3 tablespoons maple syrup

Directions:
1. Prepare the base, and for this, place all its ingredients in a food processor and pulse for 3 to 5 minutes until the thick paste comes together.

2. Take a cake tin, place crust mixture in it and spread and press the mixture evenly in the bottom, and freeze until required.
3. Prepare the chocolate cheesecake, and for this, place all its ingredients in a food processor and pulse for 2 minutes until smooth.
4. Pour the chocolate cheesecake mixture on top of the prepared base, smooth the top and freeze for 20 minutes until set.
5. Then prepare the orange cheesecake and for this, place all its ingredients in a food processor, and pulse for 2 minutes until smooth
6. Top orange cheesecake mixture over chocolate cheesecake, and then freeze for 3 hours until hardened.
7. Then prepare the chocolate topping and for this, take a bowl, add all the ingredients in it and stir until well combined.
8. Spread chocolate topping over the top, freeze the cake for 10 minutes until the topping has hardened and then slice to serve.

Nutrition:
- Calories: 508 Cal

- Fat: 34.4 g
- Carbs: 44 g
- Protein: 8 g
- Fiber: 3 g

Coconut Ice Cream Cheesecake

Preparation Time: 3 hours

Cooking Time: 0 minute

Servings: 4

Ingredients:

For the First Layer:

- 1 cup mixed nuts
- 3/4 cup dates, soaked for 10 minutes in warm water
- 2 tablespoons almond milk

For the Second Layer:

- 1 medium avocado, diced
- 1 cup cashew nuts, soaked for 10 minutes in warm water
- 3 cups strawberries, sliced
- 1 tablespoon chia seeds, soaked in 3 tablespoons soy milk
- 1/2 cup agave
- 1 cup melted coconut oil
- 1/2 cup shredded coconut

- 1 lime, juiced

Directions:

1. Prepare the first layer, and for this, place all its ingredients in a food processor and pulse for 3 to 5 minutes until the thick paste comes together.
2. Take a springform pan, place crust mixture in it and spread and press the mixture evenly in the bottom, and freeze until required.
3. Prepare the second layer, and for this, place all its ingredients in a food processor and pulse for 2 minutes until smooth.
4. Pour the second layer on top of the first layer, smooth the top, and freeze for 4 hours until hard.
5. Serve straight away.

Nutrition:

- Calories: 411.3 Cal
- Fat: 30.8 g
- Carbs: 28.7 g
- Protein: 4.7 g
- Fiber: 1.3 g

Matcha Coconut Cream Pie

Preparation Time: 5 minutes

Cooking Time: 0 minute

Servings: 4

Ingredients:

For the Crust:

- 1/2 cup ground flaxseed
- 3/4 cup shredded dried coconut
- 1 cup Medjool dates, pitted
- 3/4 cup dehydrated buckwheat groats
- 1/4 teaspoons sea salt

For the Filling:

- 1 cup dried coconut flakes
- 4 cups of coconut meat
- 1/4 cup and 2 Tablespoons coconut nectar
- 1/2 Tablespoons vanilla extract, unsweetened
- 1/4 teaspoons sea salt
- 2/3 cup and 2 Tablespoons coconut butter
- 1 Tablespoons matcha powder

1/2 cup coconut water

Directions:

Prepare the crust, and for this, place all its ingredients in a food processor and pulse for 3 to 5 minutes until the thick paste comes together.

Take a 6-inch springform pan, grease it with oil, place crust mixture in it and spread and press the mixture evenly in the bottom and along the sides, and freeze until required.

Prepare the filling and for this, place all its ingredients in a food processor, and pulse for 2 minutes until smooth.

Pour the filling into prepared pan, smooth the top, and freeze for 4 hours until set.

Cut pie into slices and then serve

Nutrition:

- Calories: 209 Cal
- Fat: 18 g
- Carbs: 10 g
- Protein: 1 g
- Fiber: 2 g

Chocolate Peanut Butter Cake

Preparation Time: 5 minutes

Cooking Time: 0 minute

Servings: 8

Ingredients:

For the Base:

- 1 tablespoon ground flaxseeds
- 1/8 cup millet
- 3/4 cup peanuts
- 1/4 cup and 2 tablespoons shredded coconut unsweetened
- 1 teaspoon hemp oil
- 1/2 cup flake oats

For the Date Layer:

- 1 tablespoon ground flaxseed
- 1 cup dates
- 1 tablespoon hemp hearts
- 2 tablespoons coconut

- 3 tablespoons cacao

For the Chocolate Layer:

- 3/4 cup coconut flour
- 2 tablespoons and 2 teaspoons cacao
- 1 tablespoon maple syrup
- 8 tablespoons warm water
- 2 tablespoons coconut oil
- 1/2 cup coconut milk
- 2 tablespoons ground flaxseed

For the Chocolate Topping:

- 7 ounces coconut cream
- 2 1/2 tablespoons cacao
- 1 teaspoon agave
- For Assembly:
- 1/2 cup almond butter

Directions:

1. Prepare the crust, and for this, place all its ingredients in a food processor and pulse for 3 to 5 minutes until the thick paste comes together.

2. Take a loaf tin, grease it with oil, place crust mixture in it and spread and press the mixture evenly in the bottom and along the sides, and freeze until required.

3. Prepare the date layer, and for this, place all its ingredients in a food processor and pulse for 2 minutes until smooth.

4. Prepare the chocolate layer, and for this, place flour and flax in a bowl and stir until combined.

5. Take a saucepan, add remaining ingredients, stir until mixed and cook for 5 minutes until melted and smooth.

6. Add it into the flour mixture, stir until dough comes together, and set aside.

7. Prepare the chocolate topping, place all its ingredients in a food processor and pulse for 3 to 5 minutes until smooth.

8. Press date layer into the base layer, refrigerate for 1 hour, then press chocolate layer on its top, finish with chocolate topping, refrigerate for 3 hours and serve.

Nutrition:
- Calories: 390 Cal
- Fat: 24.3 g
- Carbs: 35 g
- Protein: 10.3 g
- Fiber: 2 g

Chocolate Raspberry Brownies

Preparation Time: 4 hours

Cooking Time: 0 minute

Servings: 4

Ingredients:

For the Chocolate Brownie Base:

    12 Medjool Dates, pitted

    3/4 cup oat flour

    3/4 cup almond meal

    3 tablespoons cacao

    1 teaspoon vanilla extract, unsweetened

    1/8 teaspoon sea salt

    3 tablespoons water

    1/2 cup pecans, chopped

For the Raspberry Cheesecake:

    3/4 cup cashews, soaked, drained

    6 tablespoons agave nectar

1/2 cup raspberries

1 teaspoon vanilla extract, unsweetened

1 lemon, juiced

6 tablespoons liquid coconut oil

For the Chocolate Coating:

2 1/2 tablespoons cacao powder

3 3/4 tablespoons coconut Oil

2 tablespoons maple syrup

1/8 teaspoon sea salt

Directions:

Prepare the crust, and for this, place all its ingredients in a food processor and pulse for 3 to 5 minutes until the thick paste comes together.

Take a 6-inch springform pan, grease it with oil, place crust mixture in it and spread and press the mixture evenly in the bottom and along the sides, and freeze until required.

Prepare the cheesecake topping, and for this, place all its ingredients in a food processor and pulse for 2 minutes until smooth.

Pour the filling into prepared pan, smooth the top, and freeze for 8 hours until solid.

Prepare the chocolate coating and for this, whisk together all its ingredients until smooth, drizzle on top of the cake and then serve.

Nutrition:

Calories: 371 Cal

Fat: 42.4 g

Carbs: 42 g

Protein: 5.5 g

Fiber: 2 g

Brownie Batter

Preparation Time: 5 minutes

Cooking Time: 0 minute

Servings: 4

Ingredients:

  4 Medjool dates, pitted, soaked in warm water

  1.5 ounces chocolate, unsweetened, melted

  2 tablespoons maple syrup

  4 tablespoons tahini

  ½ teaspoon vanilla extract, unsweetened

  1 tablespoon cocoa powder, unsweetened

  1/8 teaspoon sea salt

  1/8 teaspoon espresso powder

  2 to 4 tablespoons almond milk, unsweetened

Directions:

  Place all the ingredients in a food processor and process for 2 minutes until combined.

  Set aside until required.

Nutrition:

  Calories: 44 Cal

Fat: 1 g

Carbs: 6 g

Protein: 2 g

Fiber: 0 g

Strawberry Mousse

Preparation Time: 5 minutes

Cooking Time: 15 minutes

Servings: 4

Ingredients:

- 8 ounces coconut milk, unsweetened
- 2 tablespoons honey
- 5 strawberries

Directions:

1. Place berries in a blender and pulse until the smooth mixture comes together.
2. Place milk in a bowl, whisk until whipped, and then add remaining ingredients and stir until combined.
3. Refrigerate the mousse for 10 minutes and then serve.

Nutrition:

- Calories: 145 Cal
- Fat: 23 g
- Carbs: 15 g

- Protein: 5 g
- Fiber: 1 g

Blueberry Mousse

Preparation Time: 20 minutes

Cooking Time: 0 minute

Servings: 2

Ingredients:

- 1 cup wild blueberries
- 1 cup cashews, soaked for 10 minutes, drained
- 1/2 teaspoon berry powder
- 2 tablespoons coconut oil, melted
- 1 tablespoon lemon juice
- 1 teaspoon vanilla extract, unsweetened
- 1/4 cup hot water

Directions:

1. Place all the ingredients in a food processor and process for 2 minutes until smooth.
2. Set aside until required.

Nutrition:

- Calories: 433 Cal
- Fat: 32.3 g
- Carbs: 44 g
- Protein: 5.1 g

Tips To Keep Motivated

Staying motivated on an exercise plan can be tough. You might start out with all of the best intentions, but after a few weeks or so, you will get worn out and not want to continue. It is much easier to just sit on the couch and hope that everything works out the way that you would like. While you know all of the great reasons to get up and do some exercising, it just is not as much fun, or at least is more work, than some of the other things you might want to do. Here are some of the best tips that you can use that will help you to keep motivated and get in a great workout every day.

Set some goals

Before you even head out to the gym, make sure that you are setting some goals. Make them challenging enough that you will need to put in some work, but simple enough that you would actually be able to get them done if you work hard. For example, it is not a good idea to say you will lose ten pounds a week, but saying you want to lose 2 pounds is reasonable.

Write down these goals from the beginning. They can

be anything that you want as long as they give you a bit of a challenge and make you work for it. You can say that you will lose a certain amount of weight over time, go by the measurements in your body, or you can even choose to go for a specific amount of time or reps. It is up to you, just make sure that you are having some fun and working hard while at the gym.

Bring along music

Getting on the treadmill and staring at a wall for 30 to 60 minutes is going to get boring fast. You might enjoy it the first few times, but after that, the activity is not going to be as much fun and you will find that your motivation starts to slip away. This is why you should consider bringing something along to do while you are working out. This can be almost anything. Many people like to bring along some of their favorite music. This allows them to have something fun and upbeat to listen to while they are working out plus can get them pumped up and in the right mood to keep going.

Do an activity you love

It honestly does not matter how much you think an activity is going to help you to lose weight, if you are not enjoying it, you are less likely to keep up with it and you are not going to lose weight. Find something that you like doing, such as biking, swimming, weight lifting, walking, running, or maybe even a group class, and then do that. Even if it is not burning as many calories as another activity, at least you are having fun. The more fun you have with an activity, the better results you will have because you are more likely to keep going with it.

Try a new activity

It is always good to mix things up when you are at the gym. Even if you love an activity, you might find that after a few months of doing it all of the time, you are getting bored with it. Plus, your body is going to become used to a certain activity and you will not get the same results if you keep doing it. Find a few activities that you enjoy, or try a few new ones, and the switch them around on occasion. This allows you to do something new, continue having fun, and you can continue seeing results all at the same time.

Find a friend

For some people, the way that they get some motivation is to find a friend who is going to work out with them. This person should be someone who is looking for the same goals and who will be able to hold you accountable to show up. When you are doing the work outs on your own, it is easy to say that you'll get to it tomorrow and then you never go back. On the other hand, when you know that someone is waiting at the gym for you, you might feel a bit more obligated to show up. Once there, you might as well get in a good work out since you went to all of the trouble. This means you get in a work out much more often than you would on your own, and the results will be much better.

Get outside

You do not need to spend all of your time inside in the gym. When the weather is nice and you are having some trouble getting to the gym, why not take a good walk outside. This is one of the best ways to get in a good workout and can help to lift up your mood because you are getting plenty of fresh air and sunlight.

Reward yourself

Whenever you are able to reach some of your goals while working out, you should take the time to reward yourself. This allows you to feel good about the hard work you are doing and even gives you something to look forward to. You should not let the award be about food since you are trying to lose weight and this can ruin your plans. But choosing to go out a night with friends, go see a movie, purchase some new clothes, or give yourself a spa day can be great incentives to keep yourself going.

Each person is going to have some of their own methods to use that will motivate them to see success. While it might be hard to get on a good workout program, it is important to find a way to get on one and stick with it for your overall health. Once you get started and do it well for a few weeks, it becomes a routine and is much easier to do. Follow some of the tips in this and see how easy it can be to get in your required work out each day.

Don't Forget To Exercise

There are several things that you can do in order to meet your weight loss goals. These include cutting back on the number of calories that you eat each day and starting a healthy exercise program are two great ways to meet your goals, especially if you combine them both together. It is still important to maintain an exercise program even after you have reached your weight loss goals in order to maintain the weight loss. After you have decided to go on a diet and start an exercise program the first thing that you will be asking yourself is how much exercise that you will need.

An important step that you should consider doing before you start any exercise plan is to talk to your doctor. They will be able to tell you if the plan is good for you, how much exercise you should do, and give you any advice and suggestions about what will work in your situation. They will also be able to do a complete checkup in order to make sure that they are no underlying problems in your health that could affect what types of exercises you are able to do.

You should consider some basic considerations when you start a diet. It is important to remember that there are no magic pills or amazing diet plans that will help you to lose the weigh overnight. Even if you do lose a lot of weight quickly on a particular plan, it is not

There are no magic exercise plans that work for everyone and help everyone to lose the weight. Each person has a different body and responds in different ways to certain types of exercise. It might take some trial and error in order to find out which exercises that you enjoy and which ones work the best for you.

If you are looking to exercise to lose weight there are some guidelines that you should follow. It is recommended by the Centers for Disease Control and Prevention that you try to get at least two hours and 30 minutes of exercise in a week in order to lose weight. This might sound like a lot but it ends up only being about 30 minutes five days a week; of course, the more exercise that you do, the greater the results of the weight loss. You will have to incorporate more exercise into your routine if you do not plan to cut back on your calories in order to see weight loss.

Some activities that you should include in your exercise plan include cardiovascular exercises such as walking, running, biking, hiking and swimming. In order to burn the largest amount of calories during your workout you need to elevate your heart rate and keep it at that rate for an extended time during the workout.

It is not a good idea to spend all of your time concentrating on aerobic exercises. While they are great for your heart and in helping you to burn calories and lose weight, you should include also other activities in your work out. These include strength training and stretching exercises, which can help make your bones and muscles stronger and help slim your waistline.

You can get just so many benefits from exercising. One of the benefits includes weight loss. Just for spending an hour doing a low impact exercise a 160 pound person can lose somewhere around 350 calories. If you decide to do a higher impact activity such as running you could lose up to 900 calories in that hour, which is way more than you need to burn in order to lose a pound per week.

Just how much exercise that you need in your exercise

program will depend on how much weight you will want to lose? If you live a very sedentary life, and you want to lose a lot of weight, you will have to include more exercise in your day than someone who has a job that keeps them moving all day. It is a good idea to start with 30 minutes a couple of times a day and slowly build up to working out between 30-60 minutes at least five days a week.

The Benefits of Exercising

Weight Loss

The first reason why many people will choose to exercise and work out is because they are looking to lose weight. Every weight loss and diet plan in the world will spell out how important it is to get in a good exercise program if you really want to lose weight. While limiting your calories can help out a lot, you are only able to limit those so much and exercising can help pick up the slack so that you are able to lose more. Pick a moderate to high intensity work out for the best results.

Heart Health

For you to really get a good workout, you will need to get that heart pumping and working hard. When the heart is functioning at this level, it is becoming stronger than ever before. When you sit on the couch, the heart barely has to move in order to get the nutrients all around the body so it is not becoming very strong. With a good work out that makes you sweat and gets the heart up a bit, you can work on its strength and become stronger in no time.

Brain Functioning

Studies have shown that getting in some exercise during the week is critical if you want your brain to function the way that it is supposed to. Exercise can help increase the flow of oxygen and blood to the brain which opens it up for working so much more efficiently. An added bonus is that exercise can help you out with your memory. This is important for those who are aging and need a bit of help recalling important events and facts. Of course, you may be able to find a lot of benefits of this as a younger person as well when you exercise right before a test and are better able to recall the facts you learn.

Stress

Stress is a daily part of life for most people and there is not much that they can do in order to get it to go away. But there are some things that you can do to reduce the amount of stress that you are feeling and to get yourself to look and feel better about the stress. Any time that the stress is starting to get too much for you, go and do a quick run or pop in your favorite work out movie. This will allow you to take a break from the stress you are feeling and you can better get back on track with other things.

Cholesterol

High cholesterol is a huge problem that a lot of people are dealing with because of the high fat diet found in this country. When you get on a good workout program, you can help to reduce the amount of bad cholesterol that is in the blood while also increasing the kind of good that is there.

Blood Pressure

When eating a diet that is high in sodium, or when you sit on the couch all day and do not perform some kind of physical activity, it is easy for you to get high blood pressure. One of the first things that the doctor is going to recommend that you do is get out and start exercising at least five days a week. This will allow the heart to function properly, your cholesterol to go lower, and your body to be better able to reduce the salts that are in there. All of this combines to allow your blood pressure to go way down.

Diabetes

Even the symptoms of diabetes can be controlled better when you are on a good exercise program. You will find that the body is able to metabolize the sugars that you are consuming much better when you are on this kind of program. Plus you are less likely to crave unhealthy and sugary foods so your insulin will not be under as much stress. If you are suffering from diabetes or pre-diabetes, it is best if you are able to get on a good workout program as soon as possible.

Mood

Your mood can be influenced by how much you exercise. Those who are depressed and down a lot of the time are the ones who rarely if ever get out there and do a good work out. Think about it this way, the few times that you have been to the gym and got in a really good workout how did you feel? Most people will say they felt good and that they were happy and on a little cloud for the rest of the day. Well, if you get on a good exercise program, you will be able to feel this way all of the time. Overall your mood will begin to improve. If you have depression, you may be able to cure it with a good exercise program. Even if you are not suffering from a mood disorder, you can benefit from the mood enhancement that comes from a good work out program.

Digestion

For many of those who are suffering from issues with their digestive tracts, a good work out program is able to help out with this. You should get in at least five days of moderate activity for 30 minutes on each day in order to see some of these great benefits on your digestive system in no time.

Self-confidence

For many, the way that they look and feel can determine how confident they are in themselves. When they start out on an exercise program and begin to lose weight, plus get all of the great health benefits that are listed above, they are going to feel a little bit better and you will notice a huge surge in the amount of self-confidence that they are feeling. They will begin to like the way that they look and will want to show it off. Just a few minutes of exercise each day can make this into a reality.

Intermittent Fasting Strategy With No Meat Diet

Fasting is not a new thing, as it has been practiced through the ages for different reasons. People fast for religious, spiritual, medical, and cultural reasons. People even fast in protest of something like the cutting down of trees in the rainforest, or the neglect of human rights.

However, in recent years scientists have become more interested in the health benefits of fasting. There are long and short-term benefits of intermittent fasting, especially when a person follows a plant-based whole-foods diet.

Some of the health benefits of intermittent fasting on a plant-based diet may include:

Age benefits — it may prolong a person's life and may have anti-aging benefits.

 Weight loss — it may help with weight loss when done in a properly controlled environment.

Sleep — it is thought the intermittent fasting helps to

regulate the circadian rhythm. The circadian rhythm is what determines the body's sleep patterns. When this rhythm is regulated, a person falls asleep a lot easier and has a better quality of sleep. A better quality of sleep means a person wakes up feeling refreshed.

Lowers the risk of disease — intermittent fasting may help to increase insulin sensitivity, prevent cancer, increase cell turnover (autophagy), lower blood pressure and cholesterol.

Brain function — intermittent fasting is thought to be able to boot brain function to increase a person's concentration and improve their mental acuity.

When we eat, our body's insulin level rises in order to store away excess energy by either:

Breaking carbohydrates into glucose to be stored in the liver of muscle.

Once the liver has reached its limit of glucose, it gets turned into fat.

This basically means that fat that cannot be stored in the liver is then taken and stored in fat deposits around the body.

When we do not eat, our bodies basically reverse the process as the insulin level will drop and the body starts to burn the stored fat for energy.

How intermittent fasting helps is to stop the body from being in the "fed" state all the time, to not being fed state. When the body is not being fed and is in a hunger state, the body starts to use up all the excess fat. Intermittent fasting helps to maintain the body's balance and clean out its pantry of stored fat (glucose). There is no actual set time limit to fast or not to fast; you can fast from 16 hours to a few days. Although if you are thinking of fasting for a few days it is advisable to do it under strict medical supervision.

You can also fast for a day, from 7 am to 6 pm. Intermittent fasting diet is usually split into the following patterns:

Fasting hours

Fasting should be done within strict daily time windows. 16-hours of intermittent fasting and 8-hours of eating. This means you have to spend 16 hours of the day not eating; you then have an 8-hour window in which to eat. It does not mean to gorge yourself for 8 hours, though. It means to eat at regular intervals, following a controlled number of calories. This is a good pattern for beginners to start with.

20-hours of intermittent fasting and 4-hours of eating. This intermittent fasting is for more advanced intermittent fasting. It requires 20 hrs of fasting with only a 4-hour eating window.

24-hour fasting should be done on one day and then the day has one meal. The day two meals, and so on.

Fasting Days

ALTERNATE-DAY FASTING

DAY 1	DAY 2	DAY 3	DAY 4	DAY 5	DAY 6	DAY 7
Eats normally	24-hour fast OR Eat only a few hundred calories	Eats normally	24-hour fast OR Eat only a few hundred calories	Eats normally	24-hour fast OR Eat only a few hundred calories	Eats normally

Daily fasting time windows should only be a day, within or for a certain period of days.

5 days off intermittent fasting and 2 days of intermittent fasting is the version that has the most medical support. This is the version of intermittent fasting a doctor may recommend if you are under medical supervision or have sought medical advice. You spend 5 days eating regularly, on a plant-based diet and 2 days of fasting following one of the time windows in the above. It should also be noted that during these

time windows of the 2 days fasting, a person should only eat around 500 calories per day.

1 day off 1 day for a week is where you would have one day of regular eating and one day of fasting. Once again, on the days of fasting, eating time windows only permit up to 500 calories a day.

Extended fasting is not recommended unless under strict medical supervision.

There are many things to consider before you attempt intermittent fasting, especially if you are going to continue exercising or have any health conditions. But when done properly with a plant-based diet, intermittent fasting can offer a person a lot of health and weight loss benefits.

Conclusion

I hope that by this point in the, you are convinced that as a vegan, you can consume the proper foods to achieve the nutrients that you need to thrive. There are going to be many doubters out there in the world—do not let them convince you that your diet is wrong. You are the only person you need to convince that a vegan diet is the best option for you.

You have made the decision to not only better your health but also make the world around you better. At this point, you are saving animals and helping the environment. Your diet choices are beneficial to you and the world around you. Now, you know just how delicious your diet can be. While some look at a vegan diet as restrictive, you know better. As a vegan, you get to have your cake and eat it as well!

As you can see, it is possible to lead an athlete life also for those who choose the vegan lifestyle.

Rather, in many respects this is a choice to be recommended given that it has many advantages (not only from a muscle and training perspective) without any obstacle concerning the required protein intake from those who play sports–even those that are very demanding or require excessive efforts.

The important thing is to always out what the needs of our organism are in order to create solid foundations on which to build and shape our body.

Using different recipes and varying the diet are great help, not only to supply our body with the necessary nutrients, but also to make more enjoyable an act that needs to be repeated often throughout the day.

As you become more comfortable with the recipes provided in this, I invite you to add some ideas of your own! The best part of a vegan diet is how versatile it can be. If you have favorite vegetables, throw them in! There is no one way to cook—make it your own and enjoy your diet every single day. I wish you the best of luck on your vegan journey. Now, let's get cooking!

Keto Diet for Vegetarian Athletes

A New Complete Diet Guide for Athletes to Improve Performances, Burn Fat and Increase Muscle Growth

Sebi Alan Guntry

Introduction

A vegetarian diet is focused on proportionately eating more foods primarily from plants and cutting back on animal-derived foods. However, it does not necessarily involve eliminating entire food groups and lean sources of protein. This means, those on a plant-based diet may still opt to eat some meat.

Going vegan, on the other hand, means being strictly against animal products in any form—from never eating meat and dairy products to not patronizing products tested on animals and not wearing animal products such as leather.

A healthy plant-based diet generally emphasizes meeting your nutritional needs by eating more whole plant foods, while reducing the intake of animal products. Whole foods refer to natural, unrefined or minimally refined foods. Plant foods consist of those that do not have animal ingredients such as meat, eggs, honey, milk and other dairy products.

In contrast, those on a vegetarian diet may still eat processed and refined foods. Vegetarians can even eat fast foods, junk food and other salty snacks guilt-free. Once you get started with this diet, you will notice a huge difference in how you feel each day. From the time that you wake up in the morning, you will feel that you have more energy, and that you do not get tired as easily as before. You will also have more mental focus and fewer mood-related problems.

As for digestion, a plant-based diet is also said to improve how the digestive system works. In fact, dieters confirm fewer incidences of stomach pains, bloating, indigestion and hyperacidity.

Then there's the weight loss benefit that we cannot forget about. Since a plant-based diet means eating fruits, vegetables, and whole grains that have fewer calories and are lower in fat, you will enjoy weight loss benefits that some other fad diets are not able to provide.

Aside from helping you lose weight; it maintains ideal weight longer because this diet is easier to sustain and does not require elimination of certain food groups.

Don't worry about not getting enough nutrients from your food intake. This diet provides all the necessary nutrients including proteins, vitamins, minerals, carbohydrates, fats, and antioxidants. And again, that's because it does not eliminate any food group but only encourages you to focus more on plant-based food products.

As you can imagine, humans have been consuming a plant-based diet before the invention of McDonald's and some of our other favorite fast-food chains. To begin our journey, I am going to start us off in the times of the hunter-gatherer. While we could go back even further (think Ancient Egypt!), I believe this is where a plant-based diet becomes most relevant.

The hunter-gatherer time period is where we find the earliest evidence of hunting. While we do have a long history of eating meat, this was a point in time where consuming meat was very limited. Of course, humans eating meat does not mean we were carnivores; in fact, the way we are built tells us differently. Yes, we can consume meat, but humans are considered omnivores. You can tell this from our jaw design, running speeds, alimentary tract, and the fact we don't have claws attached to our fingers. History also tells us we are omnivores by nature; however, the evolution of our human brains led us to become hunters so that we could survive.

The need for hunting did not come around until our ancestors left tropical regions. Other locations influenced the availability of plant-based foods. Instead of enduring winter with limited amounts of food, we had to adapt! Of course, out of hunger, animal-flesh becomes much more appealing. This early in time, our ancestors did not have a grocery store to just pop in and buy whatever they needed. Instead, they used the opportunity of hunting and gathering to keep themselves alive.

Eventually, we moved away from hunting and gathering and started to become farmers. While this timeline is a bit tricky and agricultural history began at different points in different parts of the world, all that matters is that at some point; animals started to become domesticated and dairy, eggs, and meat all became readily available. Once this started, humans no longer needed to hunt nor gather because the farmers provided everything we could desire

While starting a plant-based diet is an excellent idea and has many wonderful benefits let's be honest, you are mostly here to benefit yourself. It is fantastic that you are deciding to put you and your health first. You deserve to be the best version of yourself, with a little bit of legwork, you will be there in no time

To some people, a plant-based diet is just another fad diet. There are so many diets on the market right now, why is plant-based any different? Whether you are looking to lose weight, reverse disease, or just love animals.

A plant-based diet is so much more than just eating fruits and vegetables. This is a lifestyle where you are encouraged to journey to a better version of yourself. As you improve your eating habits, you will need something to do with all of your new found energy! It is time to gain control over your eating habits and figure out how food truly does affect our daily lives! Below, you will find the amazing benefits a plant-based diet has to offer you.

What Is A Keto Vegetarian Diet For Athletes?

Instead of focusing on the foods that you can't have, you'll be encouraged to learn how to enjoy new types of food such as nuts, seeds, legumes, whole grains, fruits, and vegetables. In the of this, you'll even be provided with a grocery list, meal plan, and the foods you should avoid and the foods you should enjoy. As I said, I'm setting you up for complete success here! When we do this together, we'll also be able to save our planet one healthy person at a time.

Unfortunately, a plant-based diet is often thought of as boring and bland. While for some people, avoiding animal ingredients is incredibly limiting, you'll soon find out that as you become more innovative with your cooking skills, you will learn to create new flavors. As you try out some of the recipes provided, you'll discover flavors you did not know were even possible.

Of course, thinking about moving to this diet is going to be your first step. While it sounds like an excellent idea, often it is difficult to know where to start. The few will introduce you to the incredible benefits of the diet, who it is for, and some tips and tricks to help you get started.

What Are Plant Foods?

You will see me refer to "plant foods" many times throughout this. When I say, "plant food," I simply mean food that isn't from an animal in any shape or form. Some of the foods include potatoes, fruits, vegetables, legumes, mushrooms and more.

Some types of foods that are often confused with plant-based foods are plant fragments and plant-based processed foods. These are refined foods including chips, oil, sugar, and all-purpose flour. While these foods technically come from plants and do not contain any animal products, they are not considered plant foods. Plant foods must be whole or minimally processed.

You might be scratching your head at this point; I will clarify with an example. An apple is considered a plant food. An apple pie is not a plant food, nor is it plant-based. That is because typically, pies are prepared with milk and eggs. Another example is frozen corn. Frozen corn is considered a plant food while high fructose corn syrup is not because the syrup contains a high amount of processed sugar. Get the picture?

What Does Plant-Based Mean?

If someone tells you that they follow a plant-based diet, this means that their diet consists mainly of plant foods. Unless you are told otherwise, you can assume that this individual avoids animal-based products like gelatin, butter, milk, eggs, and animal meat, or they eat them very minimally. These individuals will also avoid eating plant fragments and place their focus on whole plant foods instead.

There will be a learning curve if you're just starting this diet but that does not mean it is impossible. You'd even be surprised to learn which foods are plant-based and which are not. While you may need to give up some of your favorite treats, I assure you there are some delicious alternatives out there. One of my favorite aspects of a plant-based diet is that you won't have to count calories. In fact, your diet will be filled to the brim with so many nutrient-dense foods that you'll never go hungry again, provided you're following the diet the correct way.

Minimally Processed Plant-Based Foods
I know a lot of new terms are being thrown at you right

now. Although it is a lot to take in at first, keep holding on. You will soon be a plant-based expert! You must understand all of these terms before diving into the diet so that you are well prepared for success. Knowledge truly is a powerful concept when it comes to succeeding with anything in life.

While you may think you understand what minimally processed means, you may be surprised to find that certain foods are more processed than you thought. Some examples are granola bars, corn tortillas, and breakfast cereals. While they are technically accepted as plant-based, they are actually highly processed. Just check out their labels and you'll see.

Some foods that are more minimally processed include oatmeal, peanut butter, salsa, applesauce, hummus, and even guacamole. Condiments like vinegar, soy sauce, hot sauce, and mustard are also considered minimally processed.

Two food items that cause a bit of confusion are mushrooms and yeast. While they are not technically considered plants, they can be consumed on a plant-based diet.

Another food that is often questioned is bread. While bread is suitable for most plant-based eaters, you will need to read its nutrient label to make a better judgment. Some kinds of bread that are sold commercially could potentially contain stabilizers, fillers, eggs and dairy. Obviously, this would mean that the bread is no longer fully plant-based. Luckily, there are many different types of bread out there for you to try that are still within the guidelines of your diet.

Plant-Based Diet Reference

As the plant-based diet grows in popularity and is being introduced to a wider audience, some people have modified and created different versions of it to fit their needs. The following diets are the most common ones.

Veganism

Veganism is a diet that includes only seeds, nuts, grains, legumes, and vegetables. Often, you will hear vegan and plant-based being used interchangeably. We will be going over why they are not necessarily the same thing. However, in a nutshell, veganism is a lifestyle choice where an individual chooses to have no animal sources in their life from clothing to food choices. There are two main categories of veganism at this point. First, you have fruitarianism; this is a diet that consists primarily of fruit. The second is raw veganism. A raw vegan will eat foods that are uncooked or dehydrated. Obviously, both of these are very restrictive for a beginner, which is not what a plant-based diet should be.

Vegetarianism

A vegetarian will eat foods such as seeds, nuts, fruits, legumes, and vegetables, much like a vegan. They are similar in that they both do not eat meat. The main difference between a vegetarian and a vegan is that vegetarians still include eggs and dairy in their diet. There are several types of vegetarianism including ovo-lacto; includes dairy and eggs, ovo; includes eggs but no dairy, and lacto; which includes dairy but no eggs. You also have semi-vegetarians who eat mostly a vegetarian diet but will have meat on special occasions. Another version of the vegetarian diet is the macrobiotic diet. This diet consists of naturally processed foods, sea vegetables, beans, vegetables, and whole grains.

Pescetarianism

There is also the pescatarian who follows a semi-vegetarian diet but includes seafood, dairy, and eggs. As you can see, there're many different alternatives. Although a plant-based diet is not an easy change if you've had the average American diet for the longest time, its flexibility makes it perfectly do-able. As I've stated, you are being provided with all of the information you need in this to help get you started! At the end of the day, the responsibility still rests on your shoulders to put in the work and tailor your diet according to your needs and desires.

Plant-Based Benefits for the Environment

You will be learning all the incredible health benefits the plant-based diet can bring you, but it is so much bigger than that. When you switch your lifestyle to being plant-based, you are also helping to save the environment. At the end of the day, what better gift can you give your children and loved ones than a cleaner and more beautiful environment to prosper in? With so much destruction in the world today, why not do your part?

For those of us who love our planet, it is a very scary world out there! Animal and plant habitats alike are being destroyed by deforestation. On top of that, we're facing global warming. By switching to a plant-based diet, you will be cutting down your carbon footprint and helping to protect the earth for future generations to come. You would be amazed to learn how much the animal-based industry of agriculture adds to our poor earth's woes. In fact, the factory farms in the United States produce about 300 million tons of waste every year! On top of that, these farms are also polluting our air and making us sicker than ever before. If you care about the environment, there are several ways a plant-based diet can help.

Cut Your Carbon Footprint

As of right now, the United Nations Food and Agriculture Organization has estimated that the production of livestock is responsible for a whopping 14.5% of global greenhouse gas emissions. It is believed that just cattle alone, which are raised for beef and milk, are responsible for 65% of these emissions. The other sources of these emissions come from feed processing and production to keep these animals alive.

As mentioned, these animals produce about 300 million tons of waste per year. This waste is responsible for 37% of the agricultural greenhouse gas emissions. It is believed that there is a management factory farm referred to as lagoons where there are cesspits filled to the brim with this animal waste. This waste produces large quantities of methane, which is responsible for warming the earth about 20 times faster than carbon dioxide.

By switching over to a plant-based diet, you are massively decreasing or even totally cutting out animal products from your diet. In other words, you are reducing your carbon footprint by not contributing to this industry. While it may not seem like much, if everyone plays his or her individual part, it can make a significant difference.

Start Conserving Water

For most diets, it isn't specified clearly what beverages are recommended. Well, on the plant-based diet, a beverage you should be cutting down on will be milk. According to the Water Footprint Network, they have estimated that it takes around 1000 gallons of water to produce 1 gallon of milk. Also, it takes up to 6 times more water to produce 1 pound of animal protein compared to 1 pound of grain protein. More water is also needed for animal produce versus plant produce. The Twente Water Centre from the University of Twente has calculated that beef uses approximately 20 times more water than grains or potatoes.

When you go on a plant-based diet, you'd be reducing consumption of animal-products and thus, help to reduce the amount of water being used. You see, water is a very precious resource. What would happen if our children have to live in a world with no fresh water? That is why we need to pave the road towards a healthier planet today, for the sake of our future generations. At this point, it is no longer just about you or me. We must do what is best for the future of the entire human race.

Cleaner Air

Clean air is incredibly important. This is a resource that we all need to survive. Humans need it; animals need it, planet earth needs it. The manure from livestock is producing a potent form of nitrogen, more commonly referred to as ammonia. This ammonia is killing off algae, fish, and even adds smog into our cities. Studies have also found that the air surrounding factory farms have above-average levels of carbon dioxide, endotoxins, and hydrogen sulfide, and all of these are terrible for our environment. Again, switching to a plant-based diet means that you'll be helping to alleviate all these toxins from our planet.

Love Animals, Don't Eat Them!

One of the major reasons people succeed in switching to veganism or vegetarianism is due to their deep love for animals. If you are like me and you can't stand the thought of eating a living being that has some form of intelligence and sentience, then cutting animal protein out of your diet should be pretty easy. That's not all. On top of saving the animals, you'll also be helping to save the habitats of these animals. Animal agriculture is a huge contributor to desertification and deforestation of our planet. Studies have shown that animal agriculture takes about one-third of the arable land in the world. By taking up and damaging so much natural land, we could eventually see the extinction of many animal species such as sloths, red pandas, and orangutans.

The Power of Plant-based

While the animal agriculture does make up the core of our environmental issues, there are other factors leading to global warming and greenhouse gas emissions too. Similarly, there're several other contributing factors to land degradation, deforestation, and extinction. While it all does seem rather bleak, make no mistake that you still have the power to make a difference.

Two of the biggest problems we face today are global warming and eating ourselves to more diseases and even our deaths. However, the real problem is that most people are unwilling to do anything about it. What many people do not know is that we can fight against climate change, and it happens to start right on our plates. By making proper food choices, we are taking back control of our own survival, all while creating true sustainability for future generations to come.

While we may be unable to change the future of our world overnight, we cannot underestimate the power of everyday habits. By choosing one plant-based meal today, it increases the odds of you choosing a plant-based meal tomorrow and then another plant-based meal the day after. As you begin to eat healthier, you're contributing to the demand and supply for plant produce. This ensures that vital crop resources are being prioritized to feed human beings as opposed to livestock. It also lets farmers know that plant produce is in-demand and a lucrative alternative to animal products. The more people switch to a plant-based diet, the more available plant-based options will be made for us. As individuals come together, I believe we truly will be able to make a difference in this world.

Of course, these are long-term benefits. However, a plant-based diet can also benefit your personal life right now. You'll be learning just how efficiently whole foods can change your life for the better. From weight loss to improving your health conditions, a plant-based diet can change your life in ways you never even expected.

Benefits Of Keto Vegetarian Diet

Healthy plant-derived protein tends to be high in vitamins, minerals, fiber, antioxidants and various other substances that we require to remain healthy and balanced. Some kinds include considerable quantities of healthy and balanced fats, as well. Beans, nuts, seeds and entire groups of grains are all healthy plant proteins that you should consume.

Research studies have revealed that healthy plant protein, as part of a plant-based diet plan, lowered the body weight and enhanced insulin resistance in obese individuals. If you are looking to reach your healthy and balanced weight, including even more plants to your diet plan is a terrific step, to begin with.

Extra research studies have established that plant-based diet plans might decrease high blood pressure, cholesterol levels and body mass index, and minimize the risk of stroke and cardiovascular diseases. In people with Type 2 diabetic issues, a plant-based diet plan has been discovered to assist the management of blood sugar levels. An added study has revealed that an extra plant-based diet regimen might reduce the risk of creating diabetic issues.

This is a piece of motivating information for individuals currently managing several of the following problems: patients being treated for persistent illness and heart problems that consume a plant-based diet plan might not require as numerous drugs. For healthy and balanced individuals, plant-based diet plans have been connected with a lowered danger of all-cause death amongst United States adults. Thinking about all the advantages, it is understandable why medical professionals and specialized nutritionists are suggesting a plant-based diet regimen to the majority of their clients.

Why plant-based?

It bolsters your invulnerable framework. Plants have fundamental supplements that you can't get from different nourishments. The nutrients and minerals, phytochemicals and cancer prevention agents in plants help keep your cells solid and your body in balance with the goal that your insusceptible framework can work at its best.

"Plants give your body what it needs to assist battle with offing contamination," says Andrea Murray, MD Anderson wellbeing training authority. "A plant-based eating routine fortifies your safe framework to ensure you against germs and microorganisms." A solid resistant framework is basic for lessening your hazard for malignant growth since it can perceive and assault changes in cells before they can advance to sickness.

Plant nourishments lessen irritation. Plants' fundamental supplements work to determine aggravation in your body. The equivalent minor phytochemicals and cancer prevention agents that lift your insusceptible framework likewise circumvent your body killing poisons from contamination, prepared nourishment, microscopic organisms, infections and then some.

"Cancer prevention agents in plants snatch all these purported free radicals that can rattle your body," says Murray. "To diminish irritation, it's essential to eat plant-based and to tune in to your body's signs for how nourishments work for you." Drawn out irritation can harm your body's cells and tissue and has been connected to malignant growth and other provocative maladies like joint inflammation. A plant-based eating routine may ensure you since it evacuates a portion of the triggers to these sicknesses.

A plant-based eating routine keeps up a solid weight. Remaining at a sound weight is one of the most significant things you can do to diminish your hazard for malignant growth. With regards to malignancy, the main thing more significant than keeping up a solid weight, isn't smoking.

This is on the grounds that overabundance weight causes irritation and hormonal irregularity. In the event that you are overweight or fat, your hazard is higher for 12 distinct sorts of malignant growth including colorectal, post-menopausal bosom, uterine, esophageal, kidney and pancreatic diseases.

On the off chance that you eat for the most part plants,

you evacuate huge numbers of the nourishments that lead to weight gain. Include in exercise and you're a way towards weight reduction.

Plants are high in fiber. Fiber is available in all natural plant nourishments. It is the thing that makes up the structure of the plant, and on the off chance that you eat a greater amount of it you get to an entire host of advantages. Eating a plant-based eating routine improves the wellbeing of your gut so you are better ready to ingest the supplements from nourishment that help your resistant framework and lessen irritation. Fiber can bring down cholesterol and balance out glucose and it's incredible for acceptable entrail the executives.

Fiber is significant for diminishing your malignant growth hazard. This is particularly valid for your hazard for the third most basic disease: colorectal malignant growth. A plant-based eating regimen lessens your hazard for different ailments as well. The advantages of eating for the most part plants are not restricted to decreasing your malignancy hazard.

A plant-based eating regimen likewise has been appeared to diminish your hazard for coronary illness, stroke, diabetes and some emotional well-being sicknesses.

Ensure your plant-based dinners are solid

Indeed, even a plant-put together dinner depends with respect to you to maintain a strategic distance from the significant eating routine entanglements, similar to sugar and fat. Utilizing sound cooking techniques and realizing how to capitalize on your vegetables can assist you with getting every one of the advantages a plant-based eating routine offers.

This implies pan fried vegetables are out. So are profoundly prepared nourishments like saltines and treats. Point of confinement sugary treats too and ensure you are picking entire grains. Ordinary pasta, white bread and white rice might be plant items, however they are not produced using entire grains. Pick 100% entire wheat pasta and bread, and eat darker rice.

Picking plants will help all your body's frameworks work as well as can be expected.

To Motivate And Energize Your Body

There is a saying that describes breakfast as being the most important meal of the day. Why is that? After a good night's sleep, your body needs to be replenished with healthy levels to ensure the proper function of the muscles and brain. It is also partially dehydrated. The glycogen stored in the liver through carbohydrates is depleted. Cortisol levels are higher, as well. It is a hormone responsible for breaking down muscle.

According to Tim Ziegenfuss, "skipping breakfast drop kicks your coordination, stifles concentration, and puts a straitjacket on alertness." He is the International Society for Sports Nutrition's president. Then, skipping breakfast will weaken your muscle strength and endurance.

You see, breakfast is what gets your metabolism going. It is responsible for burning calories that you ingest throughout the day. On the downside, skipping breakfast will conserve calories instead. It is wrong to think that omitting breakfast means fewer calories because you risk having a higher body mass index. BMI is the ratio used to determine a person's healthy weight range. It is calculated by comparing their weight to their height. A higher BMI suggests you might be overweight. Those who eat breakfast are generally slimmer because starting the day with protein and fiber keeps your food intake in check for the rest of the day. Other advantages to starting your day with a nutritious meal are a higher intake of calcium and fiber, the consumption of additional fruits and vegetables, and better performance in the execution of tasks. The same applies to exercise. It gives you energy, helps you stay focused and get things done. Eating breakfast also is linked to lower cholesterol levels and reduced risk of getting a chronic disease. Additionally, it facilitates mental faculties, such as concentration and memory.

However, those who don't have breakfast are more likely to make unhealthy food choices for the rest of the day. There is also an increased risk of developing other bad habits and risky behaviors.

Athletes realize that the best investment they can make is their health. That means fitness enthusiasts should favor a satisfying meal over a few extra minutes of shut-eye. Saying you don't have enough time to eat breakfast, aren't hungry, or don't like eating breakfast foods are excuses that will affect your performance.

Therefore, dieticians suggest you eat a more copious breakfast, one with anywhere between 500-700 calories. Not only will it provide you with energy, but limit cravings and keep hunger at bay. On the other hand, if you plan on working out first thing in the morning, a half-breakfast will suffice. Doing so will prolong your workout and enhance your physical activity. Even a simple breakfast is better than eating nothing at all.

Oatmeal What are oats? They are considered one of the healthiest grains on the planet. They are sources of whole grains and are nutrient-dense. They also have a chockfull of vitamins and minerals, antioxidants, and fiber. Some health benefits that come with incorporating oats into your diet are a reduced risk of chronic disease, weight loss, and lower levels of sugar in the blood. Oats are good sources of fiber, protein, and carbohydrates. Antioxidants found in oats lower blood pressure.

They also contain soluble fibers that reduce cholesterol, increase satiety, and promote the growth of good bacteria in your gut.

A popular way of eating oats is in oatmeal. Here is a basic recipe for making oatmeal that you can customize to include the ingredients you love.

Casseroles

If you own a slow cooker, then you know how wonderful it is. Think of how practical it is for your food to cook overnight and be ready when you wake up the day. Breakfast casseroles can be made ahead of time. Since it is cooked in one dish, you won't have as many dishes to wash. It is quick and easy to throw together and is bursting with flavor.

In some of our plant-based recipes like this one, you will see nutritional yeast on the ingredient list. What is it? It's from the same yeast used for brewing and baking, but with added nutrients. In this guide, we recommend vegans use fortified nutritional yeast as a source of vitamin B-12 that is typically only found in meat. Vegans are more at risk of having a deficiency of this vitamin in their diet. Nutritional yeast comes in different formats, such as powder, granules, or flakes. So why is it right for you? It is a complete protein because it has all nine essential amino acids. It also has minerals that help regulate the metabolism. In addition to this, this food has antioxidants, and it can strengthen one's immunity. It helps lower bad cholesterol, too.

In this recipe, it will be used as a cheese flavoring, without the dairy. Other ways that it can be a part of your everyday cooking is as a seasoning over popcorn, in giving an umami flavor in soups or as a thickener in sauces. Just one tablespoon or two of nutritional yeast will provide you with your recommended daily amount of vitamin B12.

Muffins

These aren't your typical coffee shop muffins that you grab with a coffee to go. No, these are much healthier! Our vegan breakfast muffins are kind on the planet, too — many baking recipes animal by-products, but not when you can substitute them with a vegan egg. Simply mix one tablespoon of flaxseed meal with 2 ½ tablespoons of water.

Bran cereal is a great breakfast choice for athletes. It is jam-packed with fiber and other nutrients like zinc and copper, selenium, and manganese. Its' flavor can vary between being sweet and nutty. In recipes, it is used to add texture and taste. Bran also aids in digestion, as it helps regulate bowel movement and reduces constipation. It is rich in prebiotics, which promotes a healthy gut. Eating bran on a regular basis can reduce your risk of getting certain types of cancer and can improve cardiovascular health.

Yogurt Parfaits

What is there not to love about yogurt? It is creamy and sweet. Vegans have found a way of enjoying yogurt without dairy products. This is thanks to nuts like cashews and almonds, amongst other things.

Why is vegan yogurt good for you? Some probiotics help keep your digestive tract healthy. The nuts used to make non-dairy milk such as almonds and cashews are full of protein, fiber, and healthy fats. They also contain calcium, antioxidants, iron, magnesium, zinc, and vitamins C and E. These nutrients are beneficial for regulating blood sugar levels, decrease the wrong kind of cholesterol and help burn fat more efficiently. Regular yogurt can have ingredients like artificial coloring and flavoring, which isn't right for you. It also has dairy, which we know is a food that is responsible for animal cruelty.

To make a yogurt parfait, you simply alternate between layers of yogurt with granola and fruit. It is a feast to the eyes as much as it is nutritious. You can buy non-dairy yogurt at the grocery store. Alternatively, you can make it yourself. There are many ways to go about it, but we'll keep this sweet and simple.

Pudding

Who says that pudding is only for dessert? With the right ingredients, this snack can be turned into a filling breakfast that will kickstart your day.

Let's take a minute to talk about chia seeds. This superfood is a significant element to include in a vegan athlete's diet. They have fatty acids from Omega 3, are a good source of antioxidants and are high in iron, fiber, calcium (18% of your daily intake) and protein. In just one tablespoon of chia seeds, you have 5 grams of fiber! Chia seeds can also be mixed with water to imitate the texture and moistness of an egg.

There are several ways of eating this versatile food. When raw, it can be used as a topping in smoothies, oatmeal cereal, and yogurt. In water, the seeds will expand and get a jelly-like texture. That is because chia seeds grow in volume. It is quite impressive when you think how this small seed can absorb up to 27 times its' weight from the liquid it is soaking in.

Scrambled Eggs

Eggs are a staple item in a person's breakfast routine and are known to provide athletes with protein and other nutrients. We will show you how vegans enjoy scrambled eggs by talking about tofu. This product comes from soya. To prepare the tofu, you need to press the soy milk into a block and then cool it.

The soy milk curd is what holds it together.

ofu varies in texture and firmness. Its' origins are from China but have been embraced by European and

Western countries to promote healthy eating.

Tofu provides nine essential amino acids that the body needs to function correctly. It is also a good source of protein. Other nutrients that make tofu a popular food item in a vegan diet are its' other health benefits. It is rich in vitamin B1, copper, zinc, manganese, magnesium, and phosphorus.

Why do vegan athletes love avocados?

They have numerous health benefits, as well. Some of these include healthy fats and many vitamins. Avocadoes are good sources of Vitamin B-6, C, E, and K. They also have minerals like magnesium, potassium, riboflavin, and niacin. Plant-based foods such as fruits and vegetables are known to reduce the risk of developing chronic disease. Avocadoes do this and more. They also give you more energy, manage weight, and do wonders for your complexion. Monosaturated fats help satisfy hunger and stabilize blood sugar levels. Studies are even suggesting that avocados are beneficial for strengthening your immune system.

They are suitable for your cardiovascular health, too. The green fruit has beta-carotene, as well, which supports good vision. Vitamin K in avocados promotes bone health and can aid in preventing osteoporosis. A nutrient found in avocados, folate, helps decrease depression symptoms. It is high in fiber and can facilitate digestion.

Calorie Intake

Calories are the unit that we use to measure the intake of energy from food. That energy is what drives the human body. It allows for activities such as cellular respiration and optimal functioning of our muscles. You may have heard an athlete say that they are calorie loading before running a marathon, which is like filling the tank before going on a long road trip.

So, how many calories do you need per day? On average, we need to consume between 1,500 (for men) and 1,200 calories (for women) per day. According to the National Institute of Health, middle aged people need 2,000-2,400 calories per day (Szalay, 2015). These numbers are naturally a general measurement and will vary according to your age, current health, metabolic rate, and level of activity.

Different exercises can have different calorie requirements, and it is essential to calculate your calorie burn per day to better out how many calories you need to maintain your energy levels.

Calculate Your Calorie Requirements

There are a multitude of science-based methods to calculate the number of calories that you should specifically consume. Indeed, some of these are even easily accessible as online calculators that quite accurately determine your daily needs. The trick is to accurately consider all the variables that you personally have in your life. The average equation used for the Mifflin-St Jeor Equation looks like this:

For men: BMR (Basal Metabolic Rate) = 10(Weight) + 6.25(Height) - 5(Age) + 5

For women: BMR (Basal Metabolic Rate) = 10(Weight) + 6.25(Height) - 5(Age) - 161

This calculation will yield results for a resting body. Should you be more active, you need to multiply the results by 1.2 - 1.95 depending on the intensity of your activities.

Different activities will result in burning or consuming a different number of calories according to Harvard University. You weight and fitness also factors into this;

however, as an average guide, the following activities burn (and therefore need) an equivalent calorie intake as follows per half hour:

- Stretching: 120
- Weight lifting: 180
- Cycling: 210
- Walking: 120
- Soccer: 210
- Running: 270
- Speed cycling: 495

Hence, if you cycle for 60 minutes per day, you would need to consume 420 calories extra to the recommended 1,200-1,500 calories that you need to maintain your resting state per day. It is, therefore, possible to calculate how many more calories you need to consume in addition to your resting daily calorie intake to ensure that your body functions optimally. This will ensure that you are able to perform athletically without feeling drained. For those who lead an active lifestyle or are athletes, this is the all-important factor to any diet–getting enough calories to meet your energy consumption rate.

Today, thanks to technology, you can also use devices

such as the Fitbit, Apple Watch, or Garmin, and other apps to help you calculate your energy consumption during physical activity. This helps the athlete to better own up to their energy needs and eat appropriately.

Carbs Cycling

The body is a wonderfully balanced machine, and it can equalize and adapt to any changes that you make to your diet. Hence, when you make calorie changes to your diet, your body can easily equalize your calorie absorption to nullify the intentions behind your diet. Those dieting for weight loss can experience this quite a lot as the body begins to equalize and reduce the effects of your diet, leading to a decrease in weight loss. Carbohydrates are the major source of calories in the body. By controlling our carb intake, we can control our calorie consumption. This allows athletes to successfully manage their energy levels.

Carb cycling, sometimes also called the zig-zag diet, is when you consciously alternate your diet to have high carb and low carb days. This means that you will more actively experience the additional energy flow from the higher carb intake than you would if you only consumed a regular (or lower) carb intake. If we think back to marathon runners and cyclists who carb load the day before an event, this theory begins to make sense. By alternating between high carb days and low carb days, you would encourage your body to become more vital and less on "autopilot" when it comes to your energy consumption.

Calorie Watching - How to Achieve and Maintain a Steady Base-Line

One of the biggest concerns for non-vegans who consider becoming vegan is the possibility of feeling drained. This is a misconception and here's why:

Consider the following foods and their calorie value.

Vegetables:

Meats and animal products:

- Peanuts (3.5 oz.) = 567 cal
- Beef (2 oz.) = 142 cal
- Soybeans (3.5 oz.) = 173 cal
- Chicken (2 oz.) = 136 cal
- Grapes (1 cup) = 100 cal
- Pork (2 oz.) = 137 cal
- 1 Pear = 82 cal
- Fish (2 oz.) = 136 cal
- Pineapple (1 cup) = 82 cal
- 1 Large Egg = 78 cal

- Carrots (1 cup) = 50 cal
- Potato (6 oz.) = 130 cal
- Rice (1 cup) = 206 cal
- Orange Juice (1 cup) = 111 cal

These foods, and their respective calories, paint a completely different picture than the traditional one where athletes had to consume vast amounts of meat to be bulked in their muscles and endurance levels.

Your calorie base-line or maintenance calories would be the total calories that you would need in a day to ensure optimal functioning without gaining or losing weight. Calorie consumption can be calculated over a short period such as a week, which will give you a little bit more flexibility in your meal plans. This is why many diets feature a "cheat day" where you are allowed to consume high calorie foods such as "bad carbs."

Interestingly, peanuts are much higher in calories in terms of energy than meat. Peanuts contain twice as many calories as meat, and they are also rich in a wealth of other natural nutrients such as amino acids, protein, and fats.

Calories are not the only component to consider when

creating your vegan diet plan, as they simply cover the energy content of your food intake according to your exercise needs. You would also need to ensure that you obtain all the necessary building blocks to keep your body healthy and running optimally.

How To Increase Muscle Growth Muscle Building Formula

Your body needs certain diet requirements to build muscle. The most important is a small calorie surplus and enough protein. When you workout, you will damage your muscles, and these two factors will help your body repair your muscle tissue in a stronger way than it was before. For muscle growth, your protein intake should be between 0.8 and 1 grams/lb of body weight per day. You can absolutely get this through a vegan diet, but you're going to need to be clever. We've already gone over the reasoning behind this, so I'll keep it brief here and give you some examples you can use today.

Eat a few servings of those through the day, and you'll get a significant amount of protein very quickly. I'd recommend also tossing in a vegan protein powder supplement, the best of which are usually pea or rice protein powder. Better yet, get one that blends both. Take one or two scoops of them per day, and you'll be fine.

Keep an eye on your calorie balance. You're going to need a slight calorie surplus to gain muscle, which might be difficult, seeing as vegan diets are not known for their ability to let someone overeat. If you're having trouble and find yourself not gaining weight consistently, consider increasing your fat intake through olive oil, which is more calorie-dense than most vegan sources of carbs or protein. If you do this, make sure you still reach your macro requirements of carbs and protein per day.

Train.

Eat.

Recover.

Let's go over that one more time for the people in the back. Train. Eat. Recover. Really. It's that simple. That's literally all you need to do to build muscle. I'll go a little deeper into each of these, but this is exactly as hard as it needs to be.

Train. For workouts, I'd recommend compound exercises/compound movements. Basically, instead of working for just one muscle group, you work many, including many that you just can't with other exercises. You can lift more weight but be safe and you'll get faster growth. The biggest of these are the barbell squat, the bench press, the military press, and the deadlift.

They're best with heavyweight within reason and with fewer reps. I'll be calling these the big four because there are exactly four of them and I'm clever like that. You're going to see an increase of strength right of the bat because your muscles will be completely surprised by these four. Great! Then, you'll plateau. Don't panic. That's exactly what is expected. It happens to everyone. When that happens, you're going to need to come up with a workout plan that enables you to get stronger when adding more weight isn't an option. Just to confirm, the very much incorrect option is to overload yourself and injure yourself. I can't even begin to emphasize how important it is to do these big four with proper form and safety.

Cardio. Personally, I hate cardio with regarding passion even though it does great stuff for you, but you need to decide what your workout goals are before doing cardio. Cardio burns calories, and if you burn too much, you won't have a that important calorie surplus, and your body just can't build muscle. If you want to pack on muscle, consider eating more or doing less cardio.

Eat. Yes, I know that people like to think of calories as awful, but you need that surplus if you're going to build muscle. Your muscles don't grow as you workout. They grow after you finish, and you need to be getting the right calories and from the right places.

Recover. The fun part for many people this is the part when your body is reeling from working out, getting the necessary fuel, and doing what you want: getting stronger and building muscle. Much of this is done when you sleep, so make sure to get seven to nine hours of uninterrupted sleep per night, at least. Less than seven, and you'll be sacrificing possible progress and maybe your health in general. It'd be pretty stupid to go through all the effort of working out, then lose it because you didn't do the easiest thing on the planet: sleep.

Fat Loss Formula

Right now, google fat loss diets. I'll wait. You'll find eight hundred different, super muscular, super-fit gurus telling you that all the other diets are frauds and only theirs will work, and, what's more, it'll work in no time! Yeah... right. Don't just blindly trust these people. If you want to lose weight, it's very simple. There was actually a study done where people ate literally nothing other than Twinkies and they lost weight because they ate fewer calories than they expended. Heck, if you wanted, you could lose all kinds of weight by literally just not eating, but that's not a good plan, because it's very unhealthy.

No, what you want is not to shrivel up, but to keep your healthy mass and lose fat. There's a big difference here. If you want to do it the healthy way, look at the total calorie count, sure, but look at what's actually in there. You need healthy fats, proteins, and carbs for this to work. You need to also work out during this period, or you will lose muscle along with fat.

Well, hold on, you say. I met this guy who swore he

had a diet that could make him gain crazy amounts of muscle and lose all his body fat at the same time! Isn't that great? No, no, it is not because that guy is lying to you. Such a thing does not exist.

Ooh, here we go again, with another myth! The spot reduction myth. Have fat around your belly that you don't like Well, it would make sense that working on ab exercises would make belly fat go around faster than a chest exercise, right? Unfortunately, no, though that would be awesome. Some people lose fat faster than others in various places, and that's due to a little something called good genes, not the exercises they do. Another myth is that cardio will make you lose weight, which is sometimes true. If you're eating thousands of more calories than you should, you can do all the exercise you want, and you won't lose weight. You'll be putting it on.

You're going to need, for the cutting phase, a calorie deficit. You calculate this the exact same way you calculated the bulking diet, but with a difference. Obviously, you aren't going to add calories on top to lose weight. There are three classifications of calorie deficits:

- Small (10 to 15 percent below your TDEE)
- Moderate (20 to 25 percent below your TDEE)
- Large (More than 25 percent below your TDEE)

Some say that small is good. Others say that moderate is best. Very few say the large is a good plan. If you want to lose body fat fast, a moderate deficit of 20 percent below is probably your best option. If you have a faster metabolism, a smaller deficit will probably do the same thing while you sacrifice less strength while allowing you to eat more during your day. You need protein while cutting. Want to lose fat and not muscle? Protein. Normally, it's 0.8-1 gram of protein per pound of body weight.

Cheat Sheets

If you want spark an argument in your fitness and nutrition groups, bring up cheat sheets. Basically, let's say that you've been eating healthy for a week, but you really, really want to sneak in that chocolate bar at the end of the week. That's a cheat meal. It doesn't fall into your normal diet, but you really want it as a reward. Is it going to destroy you? No, of course not—as long as you keep your calories and macros in check.

I'm going to go ahead and say that 10 to 20 percent of your diet can be coming from whatever food you want, as long as it fits your total daily calories and proteins, carbs, and fats. Some people, and I've met several, can stick to a 100 percent diet. I can't. I know I can't. I would go insane. Most people would. You aren't a machine. As long as you stick to the basics of correct dieting, cheat meals are not going to cause you to get fat or lose muscle magically. Now, here's your test: you've been eating good, so you decide to eat an entire gallon of ice cream. Was that a good idea? Of course not, because you've gone way over your calorie balance.

And then, there are cheat days. Cheat days are a significantly worse idea than cheat meals because they can actually screw up the plan. If you eat five hundred calories less than your normal every day for a week, great. You can blow it all by eating badly for a day. It's just not worth it. None of us are machines, and it can be tempting to have cheat days, but you'll be shooting yourself in the foot. There are two ways to get around this problem: first, suffer. Second, make a diet that you can stick to.

Pea Protein Powder

Pea powder is made of dried yellow field pieces of fiber as a legume. It contains all the essential amino acids (except for methane). It's an excellent protein source for vegans and vegetarians. It's basically the vegan alternative to whey protein. You need protein for building muscle, and while you can get it from various foods, it's tricky and requires a good amount of planning and calculation... Or you could use pea protein powder with a balanced diet. It's completely vegan, and it's a high-quality protein and is extremely comparable to whey protein, and studies can prove it. Also, since it's not made from milk, it's an excellent choice for those who are lactose intolerant.

Don't use any kind of protein powder as your sole

source of protein. Maybe get a third of your diet, a half max, of your protein from protein shakes.

Are there side effects? Nope. It's very safe. If you have preexisting kidney problems, talk to your doctor first, but studies have shown it's safe for everyone else.

How to Use Creatine?

Creatine stands out as one of the very few supplements that actually does make you see more gains. Through the magic of science, it will make you stronger, and it will cause more water retention in your muscles, which you want because it makes them appear bigger and fuller. But, who cares if it isn't safe? Luckily for us, study after study shows that it's completely safe.

But what kind? There are tons of forms, but luckily, the research is pretty obvious: creatine monohydrate is the most effective form. You'll see more expensive kinds, like creatine ethyl and Ke Alkalyn (aka, buffered creatine), but they don't have any extra benefits, and they can be more than twice the price. No, here's what you have to do—traditional creatine monohydrate supplement. Make sure you look for the Creapure trademark because they will assure you that you'll have one hundred percent pure product.

When should I take it? It doesn't matter very much, seeing as it doesn't have an instant effect. Some people like to say that you should take it after your workout. These people like to cite studies that say there is better absorption after a workout, but here's the thing: in those studies, the researchers actually declared that the difference was so tiny that it wasn't statistically relevant. You do you. You take it when you can.

Vegan Food for Energy

Theoretically, every food has calories, and calories give you energy, so it would make sense that every food would provide you with energy, with very high-calorie foods giving you the most energy. This is not quite right, unfortunately, if you consider longterm effects. Fortunately for us, there are plenty of foods that can help you get energy without compromising you in the long term. Here's what to look for!

Quality carbs. Even though they aren't vital to your survival like some other kinds of foods, they're an excellent energy source, and they're fantastic for instant energy boosts. The more intense that your workouts are, the more important carbs become. Fats provide up to 90 percent of your energy during normal activities, but when you start getting into moderate and high-intensity workouts, it shifts into overdrive and carbs start providing energy. Focus on unprocessed or minimally processed carbs like pasta, whole-grain bread, brown rice, and sweet potatoes. Bonus points for being very nutritious and being high in fiber!

Fruits. They are also carbs, but they get their own because they hit a lot faster. If you need instant energy, you're not going to find a better source.

Coffee and tea. Well, duh. Tea takes longer to break down than coffee, so it's better for the long term, drawn-out a release of caffeine. Use them before a workout, and it'll increase your performance, but be careful—your body will get used to caffeine levels and you'll have to start drinking more and more over time.

Anything you're deficient in. If you're feeling low on energy, it could be a nutrition deficiency. I'm going to leave you with this: blood tests will tell you if you have a nutritional deficiency. If you live in cold places, you're more likely to be deficient in Vitamin D. Athletes are particularly susceptible to Vitamin C, magnesium, and iron deficiencies (which, fortunately, is an easy fix with a diet adjustment or with the right supplement). Vegan or vegetarian? You might be lacking vitamin B12 and calcium. If this is you, I have good news: these are common problems, and if you get rid of these deficiencies, you should expect a massive energy boost, and your quality of life will increase exponentially as such.

Losing Weight With A 3 Weeks Program

Days	Breakfast	Lunch	Dinner
1.	Chocolate PB Smoothie	Cauliflower Latke	Cheesy Potato Casserole
2.	Orange French toast	Roasted Brussels Sprouts	Curry Mushroom Pie
3.	Oatmeal Raisin Breakfast Cookie	Brussels Sprouts & Cranberries Salad	Spicy Cheesy Tofu Balls
4.	Berry Beetsicle Smoothie	Potato Latke	Greek-style Gigante Beans
5.	Blueberry Oat Muffins	Cauliflower Salad	Smoked Tempeh with Broccoli Fritters
6.	Chocolate PB Smoothie	Broccoli Rabe	Cream of Mushroom Soup
7.	Orange French toast	Cauliflower Latke	Curried Tofu with Buttery Cabbage
8.	Oatmeal Raisin Breakfast Cookie	Roasted Brussels Sprouts	Noodles Alfredo with Herby Tofu
9.	Berry Beetsicle Smoothie	Brussels Sprouts & Cranberries	Lemon Couscous with Tempeh Kabobs

10.	Blueberry Oat Muffins	Potato Latke	Portobello Burger with Veggie Fries
11.	Chocolate PB Smoothie	Cauliflower Salad	Thai Seitan Vegetable Curry
12.	Orange French toast	Cauliflower Latke	Tofu Cabbage Stir-Fry
13.	Oatmeal Raisin Breakfast Cookie	Roasted Brussels Sprouts	Brown Rice & Red Beans & Coconut Milk
14.	Berry Beetsicle Smoothie	Brussels Sprouts & Cranberries Salad	Black-Eyed Peas with Herns
15.	Blueberry Oat Muffins	Potato Latke	Cauliflower and Horseradish Soup
16.	Chocolate PB Smoothie	Cauliflower Salad	Curry Lentil Soup
17.	Orange French toast	Cauliflower Latke	Chickpea Noodle Soup
18.	Oatmeal Raisin Breakfast Cookie	Roasted Brussels Sprouts	Brown Rice & Red Beans & Coconut Milk
19.	Berry Beetsicle Smoothie	Brussels Sprouts & Cranberries Salad	Black-Eyed Peas with Herns
20.	Blueberry Oat Muffins	Potato Latke	Cauliflower and Horseradish Soup
21.	Chocolate PB Smoothie	Cauliflower Salad	Curry Lentil Soup

The Importance Of Proteins

When you start any diet, you usually do so with an end goal in mind. This goal serves as motivation to keep you on track. Unlike with most diets, a whole foods plant-based diet is not something you commit to with the mindset that you will only stick with it until that goal is met. This type of diet is more of a lifestyle change that will benefit you for years. Having an end goal of losing weight can help you get started but you need to dive deeper into what will keep you motivated and committed to this type of lifestyle.

The health benefits alone can be motivating enough, though for most this isn't enough incentive to stick with the diet for the long haul. This is especially important since your family and friends may not be on the same path as you. Finding a deeper 'why' in terms of what specifically you want to get from this diet will help remind you that you aren't just eating healthy to fit into your skinny jeans but are doing it to have more energy, less medical issues, and a better quality of life. Before you begin your journey with a whole food plant-based diet you need to clearly state why you are doing it and then commit to sticking with your 'why' for the long term.

Stock up on healthy food and eliminate unhealthy processed foods one of the first things to do when starting out on a whole foods diet is the go through your pantry and cupboards and get rid of everything that is not of nutritional value. This can be difficult for many because the thought of just throwing out food seems like such a waste. To make it easier, you can try to give these items away to friends or family or even donate them to a food shelter. Replace these unhealthy items with fruits, vegetables and beans and whole grains. If you do end up keeping the unhealthy options because you just can't bring yourself to throw it out, keep it out of sight. Keep fruits, nuts, and seeds easily accessible on the counter so you are more likely to reach for these healthier food options.

Snack healthy and make your meals at home

Fruits, vegetables, nuts, and seeds are ideal snacks that are quick to prepare or grab and go. Unhealthy snacking tends to be the number one reason why individuals are unable to lose weight or fully commit to a healthier plant-based diet. This is often because there are many triggers or habits you have grown accustomed to that make it easier to choose unhealthy options. For instance, buying breakfast or lunch instead of cooking your meals at home can hinder your results. Prepping your breakfast and lunches for the week might take a little extra work on the weekend, but it is crucial when you want to truly reap the benefits from a whole food plant-based diet.

Do one thing at a time

Making a lifestyle change is often challenging. Very few people can switch to a whole foods plant-based diet successfully. Hence, making all these changes all at once can become overwhelming or seem impossible. Instead of trying to dive right into this type of diet, give yourself time to adjust to the different foods. Begin by simply adding more fruits and veggies to your diet. Eat these items first when it comes to mealtime. Then replace your animal meats, processed flours or sugars with whole grains and natural sweeteners. Commit to eating one fully plant-based meal for the first week. Simply switching from animal products to plant-based options and swapping out processed and sugary foods with healthier options can have the biggest impact on your health.

Start your day right

One of the first meals you should try switching to plant-based is breakfast. Not only is breakfast one of the most important meals of your day, it sets the tone for the day. If you eat an unhealthy breakfast first thing in the morning, you are more likely to have an unhealthy lunch and dinner. Breakfast can also be one of the unhealthiest meals of the day as people tend to opt for quick and convenient solutions without realizing fresh fruits and veggie wraps can be just as quick and easy.

Breakfast can be the easiest meal to transition over to a whole foods plant-based diet. To make the transition easier, you can start by simply adding veggies or fruit to your breakfast. Mix in some spinach, mushrooms, peppers, and other veggies to your eggs. You can also blend a fruit smoothie or just grab a banana on your way out. These foods are filling and can make the switch to a plant-based diet easier.

Be aware of harmful chemicals and ingredients.

Not all fresh produce is treated equally. Much of the offseason items you find at the grocery store can be harmful to your health as they are treated with pesticides or other chemicals. Genetically modified organisms (GMOs) are also of great concern given their genetically engineered DNA. A GMO refers to any organism whose genetics have been altered or modified with the DNA of another organism through genetic engineering. Through this process, most crops and products have grown to be pesticide-resistant, weather resistant, and modified to grow in greater quantities. When this occurs, it can be incredibly harmful as these plants are often treated with toxic chemicals. These chemicals should kill the plant, however, because of the modifications made to the plant's genetic makeup, the chemicals are instead absorbed. These chemicals are then transferred to your own body when you consume any GMO foods.

In addition to the health risks posed by GMOs, they are incredibly harmful to the environment as they cause original nutrient-dense plants to become extinct, resulting in only the GMO versions of these plants to be available. This has become a widespread concern in many countries around the world which have already taken measures to limit or ban the production of GMO foods.

When shopping, always buy organic whenever possible. This is an important aspect of the whole foods plant-based diet as it brings awareness to the quality of foods and influences how the crops and produce are grown and how livestock are reared. Organic foods are untreated and are of the most natural state possible.

Join an online community

Joining groups with other individuals who already living a whole food plant-based lifestyle can help make the transition easier. It is a good idea to join different communities to learn more about the diet itself. Online social groups are also a great place to turn to when you need ideas for recipes, meal plans, or how to get the rest of your family on the same page as you. You can find groups that are about whole foods and plant-based diets by doing a quick search on Facebook or Instagram. Some social media groups to check out:

☐Eat to live Daily

☐My Vegan Dreams

☐Plant Based Nutrition Support Group

Get the proper tools for your kitchen

You probably already have most of the tools and essentials necessary for a plant-based diet in your kitchen. This includes things like knives, cutting boards, and strainers. There are additional tools that can make prepping and cooking whole foods more enjoyable. Rice cookers, steamer basket, blender, Instapots, and other kitchen appliances can make cooking easier. Stocking up on storage containers will help your meal prep like a pro. A whole foods plant-based diet doesn't have to be a lot of work and stocking your kitchen with the right tools will lessen the workload.

Plan ahead when eating out

A lot of people get stuck on how they can enjoy dining out when dedicated to a whole foods plant-based diet, but this shouldn't be a concern. Many local restaurants already use locally sourced foods which means they use quality products. However, this isn't always the case with chain restaurants which is something you want to keep in mind. If you are planning on enjoying an evening out, do your research first.

Look for places that specialize in vegan or organic foods. Feel free to call the restaurant ahead of time to see how your dietary needs can be accommodated. Another thing you want to do is read through as this will allow you to see what others are saying about the location and if they are willing to make menu changes to accommodate customers. Places to read can include: The restaurants social media page such as Facebook or Instagram.

- Yelp
- Zagat
- OpenTable
- Trip Advisor

Eating a whole foods plant-based diet doesn't mean your nights out need to end, it simply means finding new, interesting spots that you may have overlooked before.

Experiment, a lot!

A plant-based diet offers a variety of dishes that can be enjoyed. Many find eating most of their meals in raw form or uncooked, to be the best. Others like to steam their food, spice up their veggies, and include a variety of textures and flavors. Have an open mind and embrace a new way of cooking. Experiment with various ingredients, profiles, and styles of cooking until you find one you enjoy and can stick with for a majority of your meals. Find a few stable meals and recipes that you can use regularly, but also continue to try new things. It is also a good idea to continue experimenting, even if you have found a preference, to keep things interesting.

Keep things simple.

When you are eating a diet that focuses on consuming more plants and whole foods, counting calories is of little importance. Many people at first struggle with how much food they find themselves consuming throughout the day. Rest assured, that since most of the foods you are eating are nutrient-dense as opposed to calorically dense, it is normal to eat more. Do not worry about how many calories you consume, instead, listen to your body and avoid depriving it of food when you feel hungry. However, just be sure the foods you eat are providing value.

A plant-based diet doesn't just involve changing what you eat, it also involves changing the way you think about food. When you feel apprehensive about snacking on another fruit bowl or nuts, remind yourself that you are supplying your body with vital nutrients and vitamins that it needs, so you don't want to deprive it. Learn to enjoy the foods you are eating and let go of the idea that you have to count calories or fear how much you are eating.

Mindful eating can help you build a better relationship with the food you eat and let go of the anxiety that comes with counting calories or perfect portions. With mindful eating, you engage all your senses, you savor every bite and focus on the taste and textures as you chew. By practicing this type of mindfulness while you eat, you learn to enjoy food more as well as honor your body and health at the same time.

How to grocery shop?

When shopping you want to first buy as much of your produce from local farmer's markets. When at the grocery store, always have a list prepared so you are less likely to deviate and choose unhealthy options.

Stick to the perimeter of the store. It is the perimeter of the grocery store where you will find most of the fresh produce. This is where you want to do a majority of your shopping.

Cutting back on meat

In the Western world, meat has taken over the center stage for meals. This is why many individuals struggle with eliminating meat from their diets. When you are first starting out on a plant-based diet, you want to begin by limiting the meat products you consume and replace them with more veggies. Begin experimenting with alternative protein sources like legumes and beans. To give you a visual, picture this, instead of making meat a centerpiece on your place, use it as an accessory or decorative component.

Transitioning to a whole food plant-based diet can be fun, simple, and one of the best things you can do for your health and well-being, but you may still have some questions in the back of your mind. You have probably heard a number of misconceptions or concerns about plant-based diets.

The Keto- Vegetarian Breakfast

Chocolate PB Smoothie

Preparation Time: 5 minutes

Cooking Time: 0 minutes

Servings: 4

Ingredients:

- 1 banana
- ¼ cup rolled oats, or 1 scoop plant protein powder
- 1 tablespoon flaxseed, or chia seeds
- 1 tablespoon unsweetened cocoa powder
- 1 tablespoon peanut butter, or almond or sunflower seed butter
- 1 tablespoon maple syrup (optional)
- 1 cup alfalfa sprouts, or spinach, chopped (optional)
- ½ cup non-dairy milk (optional)
- 1 cup water

Optional

- 1 teaspoon maca powder
- 1 teaspoon cocoa nibs

Directions

Purée everything in a blender until smooth, adding more water (or non-dairy milk) if needed. Add bonus boosters, as desired. Purée until blended.

Nutrition

- calories: 474

- protein: 13g
- total fat: 16g
- carbohydrates: 79g
- fiber: 18g

Orange French toast

Preparation Time: 15 minutes

Cooking Time: 10 minutes

Servings: 4

Ingredients

- 3 very ripe bananas
- 1 cup unsweetened nondairy milk
- Zest and juice of 1 orange
- 1 teaspoon ground cinnamon
- ¼ Teaspoon grated nutmeg
- 4 slices french bread
- 1 tablespoon coconut oil

Directions

In a blender, combine the bananas, almond milk, orange juice and zest, cinnamon, and nutmeg and blend until smooth. Pour the mixture into a 9-by-13-inch baking dish. Soak the bread in the mixture for 5 minutes on each side.

While the bread soaks, heat a griddle or sauté pan over medium-high heat. Melt the coconut oil in the pan and swirl to coat. Cook the bread slices until golden brown on both sides, about 5 minutes each.

Serve immediately.

Nutrition

- calories 270
- fat 15
- fiber 3
- carbs 5
- protein 9

Oatmeal Raisin Breakfast Cookie

Preparation Time: 5 minutes

Cooking Time: 15 minutes

Servings: 2 cookies

Ingredients

- ½ Cup rolled oats
- 1 tablespoon whole-grain flour
- ½ Teaspoon baking powder
- 1 to 2 tablespoons brown sugar
- ½ Teaspoon pumpkin pie spice or ground cinnamon (optional)
- ¼ Cup unsweetened applesauce, plus more as needed
- 2 tablespoons raisins, dried cranberries, or vegan chocolate chips

Directions

In a medium bowl, stir together the oats, flour, baking powder, sugar, and pumpkin pie spice (if using). Stir in the applesauce until thoroughly combined. Add another 1 to 2 tablespoons of applesauce if the mixture looks too dry (this will depend on the type of oats used). Shape the mixture into 2 cookies. Put them on a microwave-safe plate and heat on high power for 90 seconds. Alternatively, bake on a small tray in a 350°f oven or toaster oven for 15 minutes. Let cool slightly before eating.

Nutrition:

- calories: 175
- protein: 74g
- total fat: 2g
- saturated fat:0g
- carbohydrates: 39g
- fiber: 4g

Berry Beetsicle Smoothie

Preparation Time: 3 minutes

Cooking Time: 0minutes

Servings: 1

Ingredients

- ½ Cup peeled and diced beets
- ½ Cup frozen raspberries
- 1 frozen banana
- 1 tablespoon maple syrup
- 1 cup unsweetened soy or almond milk
- Directions

- Combine all the Ingredients in a blender and blend until smooth.

Nutrition

- calories 270
- fat 15
- fiber 3
- carbs 5
- protein 9

Blueberry Oat Muffins

Preparation Time: 10 minutes

Cooking Time: 20 minutes

Servings: 12 muffins

Ingredients

- 2 tablespoons coconut oil or vegan margarine, melted, plus more for preparing the muffin tin
- 1 cup quick-cooking oats or instant oats
- 1 cup boiling water
- ½ Cup nondairy milk
- ¼ Cup ground flaxseed
- 1 teaspoon vanilla extract
- 1 teaspoon apple cider vinegar
- 1½ cups whole-grain flour
- ½ Cup brown sugar
- 2 teaspoons baking soda
- Pinch salt
- 1 cup blueberries

Directions

Preheat the oven to 400°f.

Coat a muffin tin with coconut oil, line with paper muffin cups, or use a nonstick tin.

In a large bowl, combine the oats and boiling water. Stir so the oats soften. Add the coconut oil, milk, flaxseed, vanilla, and vinegar and stir to combine. Add the flour, sugar, baking soda, and salt. Stir until just combined. Gently fold in the blueberries. Scoop the muffin mixture into the prepared tin, about ⅓ cup for each muffin.

Bake for 20 to 25 minutes, until slightly browned on top and springy to the touch. Let cool for about 10 minutes. Run a dinner knife around the inside of each cup to loosen, then tilt the muffins on their sides in the muffin wells so air gets underneath. These keep in an airtight container in the refrigerator for up to 1 week or in the freezer indefinitely.

Nutrition:

- calories: 174
- protein: 5g
- total fat: 3g
- saturated fat:2g
- carbohydrates: 33g
- fiber: 4g

The Keto-Vegetarian Lunch

Cauliflower Latke

Preparation Time: 15 minutes

Cooking Time: 30 minutes

Servings: 4

Ingredients

- 12 oz. cauliflower rice, cooked
- 1 egg, beaten
- 1/3 cup cornstarch
- Salt and pepper to taste
- ¼ cup vegetable oil, divided
- Chopped onion chives

Direction

Squeeze excess water from the cauliflower rice using paper towels.

Place the cauliflower rice in a bowl.

Stir in the egg and cornstarch.

Season with salt and pepper.

Pour 2 tablespoons of oil into a pan over medium heat.

Add 2 to 3 tablespoons of the cauliflower mixture into the pan.

Cook for 3 minutes per side or until golden.

Repeat until you've used up the rest of the batter.

Garnish with chopped chives.

Nutrition

- Calories: 209
- Total fat: 15.2g
- Saturated fat: 1.4g
- Cholesterol: 47mg 22

Roasted Brussels Sprouts

Preparation Time: 30 minutes

Cooking Time: 20 minutes

Servings: 4

Ingredients

- 1 lb. Brussels sprouts, sliced in half
- 1 shallot, chopped
- 1 tablespoon olive oil
- Salt and pepper to taste
- 2 teaspoons balsamic vinegar

- ¼ cup pomegranate seeds
- ¼ cup goat cheese, crumbled

Direction

Preheat your oven to 400 degrees F.

Coat the Brussels sprouts with oil.

Sprinkle with salt and pepper.

Transfer to a baking pan.

Roast in the oven for 20 minutes.

Drizzle with the vinegar.

Sprinkle with the seeds and cheese before serving.

Nutrition

- Calories: 117
- Total fat: 5.7g
- Saturated fat: 1.8g
- Cholesterol: 4mg

Brussels Sprouts & Cranberries Salad

Preparation Time: 10 minutes

Cooking Time: 10 minutes

Servings: 6

Ingredients

- 3 tablespoons lemon juice
- ¼ cup olive oil
- Salt and pepper to taste
- 1 lb. Brussels sprouts, sliced thinly
- ¼ cup dried cranberries, chopped
- ½ cup pecans, toasted and chopped
- ½ cup Parmesan cheese, shaved

Direction

Mix the lemon juice, olive oil, salt and pepper in a bowl. Toss the Brussels sprouts, cranberries and pecans in this mixture. Sprinkle the Parmesan cheese on top.

Nutrition

- Calories 245

- Total Fat 18.9 g
- Saturated Fat 9 g
- Cholesterol 3 mg

Potato Latke

Preparation Time: 15 minutes

Cooking Time: 10 minutes

Servings: 6

Ingredients

- 3 eggs, beaten
- 1 onion, grated
- 1 ½ teaspoons baking powder
- Salt and pepper to taste
- 2 lb. potatoes, peeled and grated
- ¼ cup all-purpose flour
- 4 tablespoons vegetable oil
- Chopped onion chives

Direction

Preheat your oven to 400 degrees F.

In a bowl, beat the eggs, onion, baking powder, salt and pepper.

Squeeze moisture from the shredded potatoes using paper towel.

Add potatoes to the egg mixture.

Stir in the flour.

Pour the oil into a pan over medium heat.

Cook a small amount of the batter for 3 to 4 minutes per side.

Repeat until the rest of the batter is used.

Garnish with the chives.

Nutrition

- Calories: 266
- Total fat: 11.6g
- Saturated fat: 2g
- Cholesterol: 93mg

Broccoli Rabe

Preparation Time: 15 minutes

Cooking Time: 15 minutes

Servings: 8

Ingredients

- 2 oranges, sliced in half
- 1 lb. broccoli rabe
- 2 tablespoons sesame oil, toasted
- Salt and pepper to taste
- 1 tablespoon sesame seeds, toasted

Direction

Pour the oil into a pan over medium heat.

Add the oranges and cook until caramelized.

Transfer to a plate.

Put the broccoli in the pan and cook for 8 minutes.

Squeeze the oranges to release juice in a bowl.

Stir in the oil, salt and pepper.

Coat the broccoli rabe with the mixture.

Sprinkle seeds on top.

Nutrition

- Calories: 59

- Total fat: 4.4g
- Saturated fat: 0.6g
- Sodium: 164mg

The Keto-Vegetarian Dinner

Noodles Alfredo with Herby Tofu

Preparation Time: 10 minutes

Cooking Time: 5 minutes

Servings: 4

Ingredients

- 2 tbsp vegetable oil
- 2 (14 oz.) blocks extra-firm tofu, pressed and cubed
- 12 ounces eggless noodles
- 1 tbsp dried mixed herbs
- 2 cups cashews, soaked overnight and drained
- ¾ cups unsweetened almond milk
- ½ cup nutritional yeast
- 4 garlic cloves, roasted (roasting is optional but highly recommended)
- ½ cup onion, coarsely chopped
- 1 lemon, juiced
- ½ cup sun-dried tomatoes
- Salt and black pepper to taste
- 2 tbsp chopped fresh basil leaves to garnish

Directions

Heat the vegetable oil in a large skillet over medium heat.

Season the tofu with the mixed herbs, salt, black pepper, and fry in the oil until golden brown. Transfer to a paper-towel-lined plate and set aside. Turn the heat off.

In a blender, combine the almond milk, nutritional yeast, garlic, onion, and lemon juice. Set aside.

Reheat the vegetable oil in the skillet over medium heat and sauté the noodles for 2 minutes. Stir in the sundried tomatoes and the cashew (Alfredo) sauce. Reduce the heat to low and cook for 2 more minutes.

If the sauce is too thick, thin with some more almond milk to your desired thickness.

Dish the food, garnish with the basil and serve warm.

Nutrition

- Calories: 156
- Fat: 8.01g
- Carbohydrate: 20.33g
- Protein: 1.98g
- Sugar: 0.33g
- Cholesterol: 0mg

Lemon Couscous with Tempeh Kabobs

Preparation Time: 2 hours 15 minutes

Cooking Time: 2 hours

Servings: 4

Ingredients

- For the tempeh kabobs:
- 1 ½ cups of water

- 10 oz. tempeh, cut into 1-inch chunks
- 1 red onion, cut into 1-inch chunks
- 1 small yellow squash, cut into 1-inch chunks
- 1 small green squash, cut into 1-inch chunks
- 2 tbsp. olive oil
- 1 cup sugar-free barbecue sauce
- 8 wooden skewers, soaked
- For the lemon couscous:
- 1 ½ cups whole wheat couscous
- 2 cups of water
- Salt to taste
- ¼ cup chopped parsley
- ¼ chopped mint leaves
- ¼ cup chopped cilantro
- 1 lemon, juiced
- 1 medium avocado, pitted, sliced and peeled

Directions

For the tempeh kabobs:

Boil the water in a medium pot over medium heat. Once boiled, turn the heat off, and put the tempeh in it. Cover the lid and let the tempeh steam for 5 minutes (this is to remove its bitterness). Drain the tempeh after.

After, pour the barbecue sauce into a medium bowl, add the tempeh, and coat well with the sauce. Cover the bowl with plastic wrap and marinate for 2 hours.

After 2 hours, preheat a grill to 350 F.

On the skewers, alternately thread single chunks of the tempeh, onion, yellow squash, and green squash until the ingredients are exhausted.

Lightly grease the grill grates with olive oil, place the skewers on top and brush with some barbecue sauce. Cook for 3 minutes on each side while brushing with more barbecue sauce as you turn the kabobs.

Transfer to a plate for serving.

For the lemon couscous:

Meanwhile, as the kabobs cooked, pour the couscous, water, and salt into a medium bowl and steam in the microwave for 3 to 4 minutes. Remove the bowl from the microwave and allow slight cooling.

Stir in the parsley, mint leaves, cilantro, and lemon juice.

Garnish the couscous with the avocado slices and serve with the tempeh kabobs.

Nutrition

- calories 270
- fat 15
- fiber 3
- carbs 5
- protein 9

Portobello Burger with Veggie Fries

Preparation Time: 45 min

Cooking Time: 30 min

Servings: 4

Ingredients

For the veggie fries:

- 3 carrots, peeled and julienned
- 2 sweet potatoes, peeled and julienned
- 1 rutabaga, peeled and julienned
- 2 tsp olive oil
- ¼ tsp paprika
- Salt and black pepper to taste

For the Portobello burgers:

- 1 clove garlic, minced
- ½ tsp salt
- 2 tbsp. olive oil
- 4 whole-wheat buns
- 4 Portobello mushroom caps
- ½ cup sliced roasted red peppers

- 2 tbsp. pitted Kalamata olives, chopped
- 2 medium tomatoes, chopped
- ½ tsp dried oregano
- ¼ cup crumbled feta cheese (optional)
- 1 tbsp. red wine vinegar
- 2 cups baby salad greens
- ½ cup hummus for serving

Directions

For the veggie fries:

Preheat the oven to 400 F.

Spread the carrots, sweet potatoes, and rutabaga on a baking sheet and season with the olive oil, paprika, salt, and black pepper. Use your hands to rub the seasoning well onto the vegetables. Bake in the oven for 20 minutes or until the vegetables soften (stir halfway).

When ready, transfer to a plate and use it for serving.

For the Portobello burgers:

Meanwhile, as the vegetable roast, heat a grill pan over medium heat.

Use a spoon to crush the garlic with salt in a bowl.

Stir in 1 tablespoon of the olive oil.

Brush the mushrooms on both sides with the garlic mixture and grill in the pan on both sides until tender, 8 minutes. Transfer to a plate and set aside.

Toast the buns in the pan until crispy, 2 minutes. Set aside in a plate.

In a bowl, combine the remaining ingredients except for the hummus and divide on the bottom parts of the buns.

Top with the hummus, cover the burger with the top parts of the buns and serve with the veggie fries.

Nutrition

- Calories; 21g
- Fat; 4.7g
- Carbs; 44.2g
- Protein; 0
- 0.5g Sugars

Thai Seitan Vegetable Curry

Preparation Time: 20 minutes

Cooking Time: 15 minutes

Servings: 4

Ingredients

- 1 tbsp vegetable oil
- 4 cups diced seitan
- 1 cup sliced mixed bell peppers
- ½ cup onions diced
- 1 small head broccoli, cut into florets
- 2 tbsp Thai red curry paste
- 1 tsp garlic puree
- 1 cup unsweetened coconut milk
- 2 tbsp vegetable broth
- 2 cups spinach
- Salt and black pepper to taste

Directions

Heat the vegetable oil in a large skillet over medium

heat and fry the seitan until slightly dark brown. Mix in the bell peppers, onions, broccoli, and cook until softened, 4 minutes.

Mix the curry paste, garlic puree, and 1 tablespoon of coconut milk. Cook for 1 minute and stir in the remaining coconut milk and vegetable broth. Simmer for 10 minutes.

Stir in the spinach to wilt and season the curry with salt and black pepper.

Serve the curry with steamed white or brown rice.

Nutrition

calories 270,

fat 15,

fiber 3,

carbs 5,

protein 9

Tofu Cabbage Stir-Fry

Preparation Time: 15 minutes

Cooking Time: 10 minutes

Servings: 4

Ingredients

- 5 oz. vegan butter
- 2 ½ cups baby bok choy, quartered lengthwise
- 8 oz sliced mushrooms

- 2 cups extra-firm tofu, pressed and cubed
- Salt and black pepper to taste
- 1 tsp onion powder
- 1 tsp garlic powder
- 1 tbsp plain vinegar
- 2 garlic cloves, minced
- 1 tsp chili flakes
- 1 tbsp fresh ginger, grated
- 3 scallions, sliced
- 1 tbsp sesame oil
- 1 cup vegan mayonnaise
- Wasabi paste to taste
- Cooked white or brown rice (1/2 cup per person)

Directions

Melt half of the vegan butter in a wok and sauté the bok choy until softened, 3 minutes.

Season with salt, black pepper, onion powder, garlic powder, and vinegar. Sauté for 2 minutes to combine the flavors and plate the bok choy.

Melt the remaining vegan butter in the wok and sauté the garlic, mushrooms, chili flakes, and ginger until fragrant.

Stir in the tofu and cook until browned on all sides. Add the scallions and bok choy, heat for 2 minutes and drizzle in the sesame oil.

In a small bowl, mix the vegan mayonnaise and wasabi, and mix into the tofu and vegetables. Cook for 2 minutes and dish the food.

Serve warm with steamed rice.

Nutrition

- Calories; 21g
- Fat; 4.7g
- Carbs; 44.2g
- Protein; 0

CPSIA information can be obtained
at www.ICGtesting.com
Printed in the USA
BVHW072306230221
600901BV00004B/167

9 781914 393129